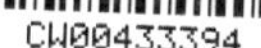

CMILLAN

Cheryl Pelteret

Activity Book

Macmillan Education
Between Towns Road, Oxford OX4 3PP
A division of Macmillan Publishers Limited
Companies and representatives throughout the world

ISBN 978-0-230-53379-0

Original design by Wild Apple Design
Page make-up by David and Jenny Hunter
Illustrated by Juliet Breese, Russ Daff, Mark Davis, Chris Pavely, Jorge Santillan and Simon Smith
Cover design by Designers Collective

The authors and publishers would like to thank the following for permission to reproduce their photographic materials:
Alamy/Stania Kasula p26(tr), Alamy/Mob Images p26(tl), Alamy/Ferdinand Reus p5, Alamy/Adrian Sherrat p34(tr), Alamy/Yiap Events p40; **Brithdir Mawr Community** p50; **Corbis**/ Kieran Doherty p18(b), Corbis/Rick Gomez p38(cr), Corbis Klaus Mellenthin p26(cl), Corbis/ Anthony Redpath p34(tl), Corbis/Anne-Marie Webber p4(br); **Getty Images**/Matt Cardy p58(b); **Hotel Kakslauttanen** p58(a); **Jumbohostel.com** p58(c); **PA Photos**/Associated Press pp4(bl), 64, PA Photos/Gareth Copley p18(tl); **PhotoAlto** p26(cr); **Photodisc** p10; **Via-Cornwall** p49.

Printed and bound in Thailand

2015 2014 2013 2012 2011
10 9 8 7 6 5 4 3 2

Hot Spot Activity Book 3

Contents

Module 1
Me and my world

1 Where I live

1 Vocabulary

Find six words in the wordsnake. Use the words to complete the sentences.

clap hibernatedivercreekworryfarmer

1 I'm a good *diver*. I practise every day at the swimming pool.
2 Bears .... in the winter.
3 Don't ....! The dog is very friendly.
4 I love cows, pigs and sheep. I want to be a .... when I grow up.
5 We often go swimming in the .... behind our house.
6 When you like something a lot, you .... your hands.

2 Grammar and vocabulary

Use the words in the box to complete the email.

clap ~~come~~ hears hibernate is live sleep swim walks worry

Where I live

To: Alison
From: Nicole
Subject: Where I live

Dear Alison,

I [1] *come* from Canada. Behind my house, there is a forest and a creek. Lots of bears [2] .... in the forest and [3] .... in the creek. Bears [4] .... in trees in the summer. When there [5] .... a bear in the garden, we [6] .... our hands. When it [7] .... that sound, it [8] .... away. We don't [9] .... about bears in the winter because they [10] .... then. Write and tell me about the animals where you live.

Nicole

Nicole

3 Grammar and reading

Put the words in the correct order to make questions. Then look at Activity 2 and match the questions with the answers.

1 Nicole / where / come from / does
Where does Nicole come from ?
2 do / the bears / where / swim
.... ?
3 in the summer / do / where / sleep / bears
.... ?
4 clap / when / they / their hands / do
.... ?
5 when / hibernate / bears / do
.... ?

a when there is a bear in the garden
b in trees
c in the winter
d Canada
e in the creek

4 Grammar

Complete the text. Use the correct form of the verbs in brackets.

Soraya [1] *comes* (come) from Ghana. She [2] .... (live) with her family in a village. People in Soraya's village [3] .... (like) to be good neighbours. When someone [4] .... (build) a new house, they all [5] .... (help). Soraya [6] .... (not go) to school in the afternoon. After school, she [7] .... (play) with her friends. They [8] .... (not have) a TV, but they all [9] .... (listen) to the radio.

Soraya

5 Grammar and reading

Choose the correct words. Look at Activity 4 and answer the questions.

1 Where **do/does** Soraya come from?
Ghana
2 Where **do/does** her family live?
....
3 What **do/does** people like to be?
....
4 What **do/does** Soraya do after school?
....
5 What **do/does** they listen to?
....

6 Vocabulary

Match the verbs with the nouns.

1 play [e]
2 build [ ]
3 help [ ]
4 listen [ ]
5 go to [ ]
6 swim [ ]
7 clap [ ]

a to the radio
b in the creek
c a house
d your hands
e with friends
f your neighbours
g school

2 Charlie's busy week

1 Vocabulary

Read the clues and write the words. Complete the crossword.

Jess

Rory

Delia

Cassie

Connor

Next Friday …

Jess is practising her [1] *sketch* for the English lesson.

Rory is seeing the [2] .... because he's got a bad tooth! So he isn't going to the [3] .... to see the new *James Bond* film.

Delia is playing [4] .... on the school team.

Cassie and her family are going [5] .... for the weekend.

Connor is watching a football [6] .... on TV.

1 S K E T C H

2 _ E _ _ _ _ _

3 C _ _ _ _ _

4 _ _ _ _ _ _ _

5

6

2 Grammar and reading

a) **Read Emma's and Ollie's calendars. Complete the text.**

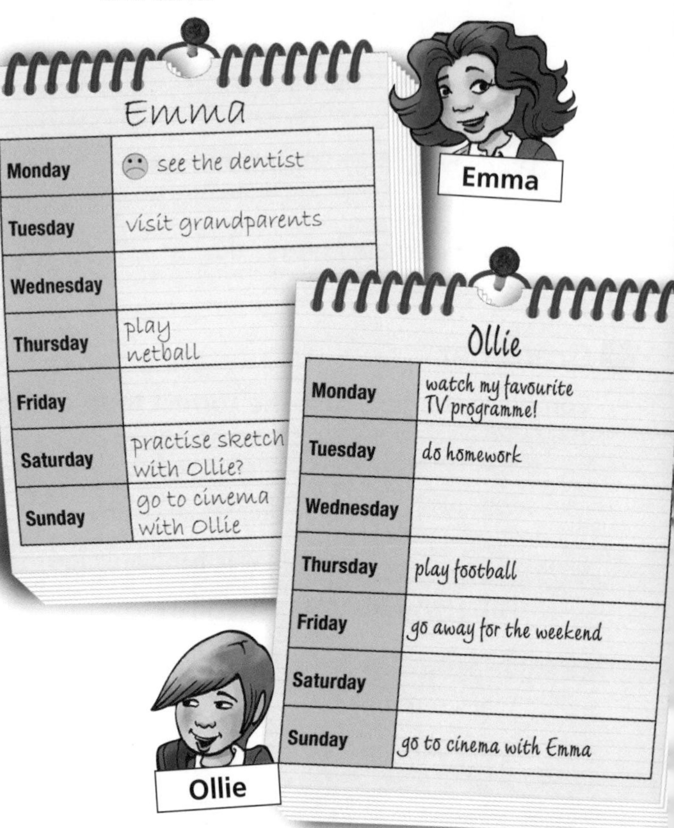

On Monday, Ollie [1] *is watching* TV. Emma [2] .... the dentist. On Tuesday, Ollie [3] .... his homework and Emma [4] .... her grandparents. On Thursday, they [5] .... football and netball. They can't practise their sketch at the weekend because Ollie [6] .... away. Are they [7] .... it on Sunday night? No, they aren't because they [8] .... to the cinema then!

b) **Read again. Answer the questions.**

1 Is Emma visiting her grandparents on Tuesday?
Yes, she is.

2 Is Ollie doing his homework on Tuesday?
....

3 Is Ollie seeing the dentist?
....

4 Are Ollie and Emma practising their sketch on Saturday?
....

3 Grammar

Use the words to write the conversation.

A: What / you / do / on Friday
[1] *What are you doing on Friday* ?

B: I / go / to Paul's house
[2] .

A: What / you / do / with Paul
[3] ?

B: We / watch / a DVD
[4] .

A: What / you / do / on Saturday
[5] ?

B: I / visit / my grandma
[6] .

A: When / you / come back
[7] ?

B: On Sunday. Why?

A: Because I / have / a party / on Sunday night
[8]
. Are you free?

B: Yes, I am. Thanks!

4 Grammar

Use the words in the box to complete the conversation.

theirs	hers	~~yours~~	ours	mine	his

Miss Bright: Whose book is this? Is it [1] *yours* , Jack?

Jack: No, it isn't [2] . Christina's got the same book. Perhaps it's [3] ?

Miss Bright: Christina, is this your book?

Christina: No, it isn't. Peter's got the same book. Perhaps it's [4] ?

Miss Bright: Peter, is this your book?

Peter: No, it isn't. Tom and Jo have got the same book. Perhaps it's [5] ?

Tom & Jo: No, it isn't, Miss. We've got [6] here!

Jack: Is there a name inside the book?

Miss Bright: Mmm, yes … there is. It's mine!

5 Grammar

Complete the conversations. Use possessive pronouns.

3 The cheapest shirts in town

1 Vocabulary

Use the words in the box to complete the conversation.

too big size is this the pattern It's large ~~are cheaper~~ looks horrible

2 Grammar

How do you make the comparative form of these adjectives? Complete the chart.

~~cheap~~ tidy new interesting tall friendly nice beautiful expensive

adjective + *er* / + *r*	adjective - *y* + *ier*	*more* + adjective
cheap		

3 Grammar

Complete the sentences. Use the comparative form of the adjectives in brackets.

1 This chair is *more comfortable* (comfortabl than that one.

2 My room is .... (messy) than my brother's room.

3 Maria is .... (bad) at English than Paul.

4 History is .... (useful) than Maths.

5 The new shopping centre is .... (modern) than the old one.

6 I am .... (old) than my brothe

4 Grammar

Write the superlative form of the adjectives.

1 messy *the messiest*
2 expensive ....
3 good ....
4 horrible ....
5 large ....
6 small ....
7 ugly ....
8 comfortable ....
9 bad ....
10 beautiful ....

5 Grammar

Complete the sentences. Use the comparative or superlative form of the adjectives in brackets.

1 A Porsche is *more expensive* than other cars. (expensive)
2 Which one do you like the ....? (good)
3 I think this is the .... dress in the shop. (pretty)
4 Today is much .... than yesterday. (hot)
5 I'm always .... on a Friday than on a Monday! (happy)
6 What's the .... joke you know? (funny)

6 Grammar and writing

Write about the teapots. Use the comparative and superlative form of the adjectives in brackets.

1 *Teapot a is the oldest. It's older than teapots b and c.* (old)
2 .... (small)
3 .... (expensive)
4 .... (cheap)
5 .... (big)
6 .... (modern)

7 Writing

Write sentences about you and your family or friends. Use the comparative and superlative form of the adjectives in the box.

young	old	helpful	lazy	tall	short	quiet	noisy

I am younger than Stephan, but William is the youngest in our family.

....

....

....

....

4 Looking after your pet

1 Reading and vocabulary

a) Read about some unusual pets. Match the descriptions with the pictures.

1 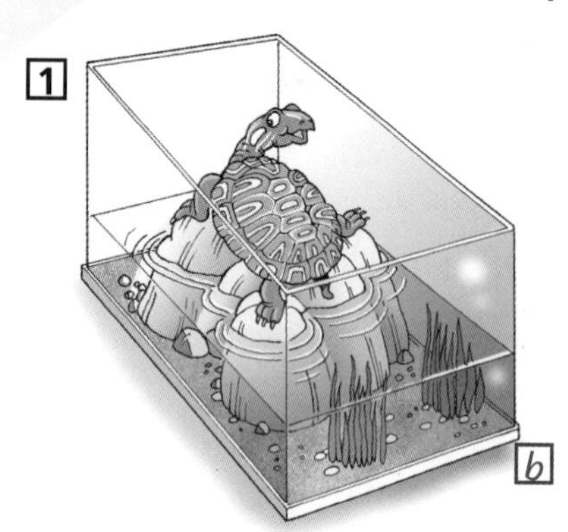
b

2 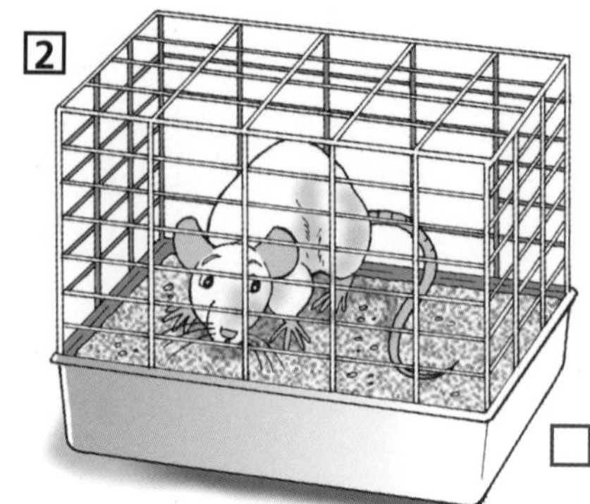

3 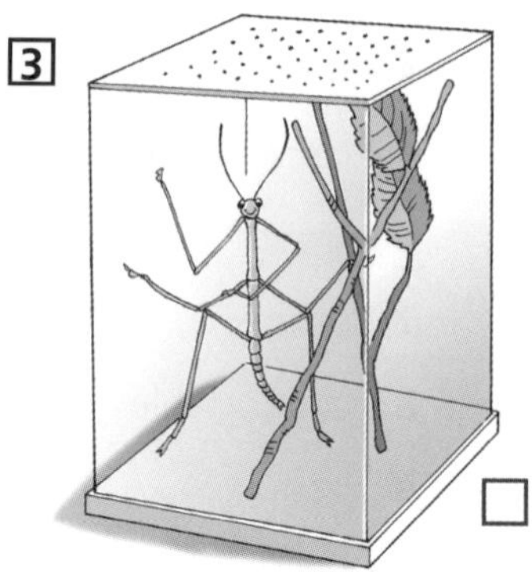

a Stick insects are brown or green. They usually live for one year. Stick insects like a big warm cage. Feed them every day. They eat leaves. Stick insects are not strong, so be careful when you hold them.

b A pet turtle lives in a large glass aquarium. It likes clean water. Put a stone or a rock inside the aquarium. Feed your turtle lots of different food – leaves, insects and worms. Turtles can live for forty years.

c A pet mouse lives in a cage. Mice like to be warm. They sleep on sawdust. Clean the cage often. They eat fruit and vegetables, and they like clean water. They like playing with toys, too!

b) Read again. Are the sentences true (T) or false (F)?

1 Stick insects eat sticks. *F*
2 Stick insects are strong insects. ....
3 A turtle lives longer than a stick insect. ....
4 A turtle lives in a cage. ....
5 Mice don't like to be cold. ....
6 Mice like to play with toys. ....

2 Writing

Read the notes. Then write about ferrets.

lives for 5–10 years	eats cat food
likes lots of exercise	likes lots of clean water
sleeps in a cage	

A ferret lives for five to ten years.

....

....

....

....

....

....

Module 1 Learning diary

Name .... Date ....

Study tip
Vocabulary

Write new words in pairs in your notebook. For example, write adjectives with their opposites.

cheap – expensive   big – small

Write these words in pairs of opposites.

~~tall~~ boring messy interesting tidy ~~short~~

1 *tall* – *short*
2 .... – ....
3 .... – ....

Check you can do these things:

1 I can talk about the lives of other children. ☐

Circle the mistakes and write the correct words.

1 Soraya (come) from Ghana. *comes*
2 Soraya and her family lives in a village. ....
3 Soraya have a TV. ....
4 Soraya's neighbours aren't friendly and helpful. ....
5 Soraya goes to school in the afternoon. ....

2 I can talk about future arrangements. ☐

Use the words to write questions and sentences.

1 What / you / do / on Saturday
What are you doing on Saturday?
2 you / play / football / after school
..........?
3 I / go / to the sports centre / tomorrow
....
4 Rory / visit / his aunt / on Sunday
....
5 We / go / to the cinema / tonight
....

3 I can compare things. ☐

Complete the sentences with the comparative or superlative form of the adjectives in brackets.

1 Ronaldo is the *friendliest* (friendly) boy in the class.
2 Who is the .... (young) in your family?
3 My lunch is .... (cheap) than my friend's lunch.
4 I am the .... (good) in my class at P.E.
5 Who is .... (beautiful) – Angelina Jolie or Charlize Theron?

4 I can talk about possessions. ☐

Use the words in the box to complete the sentences.

yours ~~his~~ mine hers ours

1 That ball is Ivan's. It's *his*.
2 Please give me that book. It's ....
3 Can you give this letter to Mary? It's ....
4 'Those sweets are ....!' said the children.
5 This is my seat and this is ...., Nick.

Module 2
Playing games and sports

5 Sports day

❶ Vocabulary

a) Look at the picture. Use the words in the box to complete the sentences.

metre race swimming race long jump obstacle course javelin

1 Cassie won the j a v e l i n.
2 Rory came second in the ________ ____.
3 Delia came third in the 100-_____ ____.
4 Connor came fourth in the ________ ______.
5 Jess came fifth in the ____ ____.

b) Write the shaded letters. Who won the long jump?

_ _ _ _ _

❷ Grammar

Complete the conversation. Use the past simple form of the verbs in brackets.

Emma: Hello, Ollie! How [1] *was* (be) Sports day?
Ollie: Not bad. The swimming event was OK. I [2] .... (swim) in the swimming race and I came first!
Emma: That's amazing! Did you throw the javelin, too?
Ollie: Yes, I [3] .... (throw) it 21 metres.
Emma: Wow! Did you break the record?
Ollie: No, I [4] .... (not break) the record, but I [5] .... (break) my arm!
Emma: What [6] .... (happen)?
Ollie: I [7] .... (run) to do the long jump. I was really fast, but then I [8] .... (fall) over!
Emma: Oh, no! So you [9] .... (not get) a medal …
Ollie: No, but I [10] .... (get) a cold drink and a biscuit!

3 Reading and grammar

Look at the picture in Activity 1. Read the article in the school magazine. Use the words in the box to correct the mistakes.

jump do the obstacle course
~~swim in the swimming race~~
throw the javelin
run in the 100-metre race

Sports Day News!

On Saturday it was our Sports day. What a fantastic day!

Rory did the long jump. Cassie swam in the swimming race. Delia threw the javelin and Connor ran in the 100-metre race. He broke the record! But poor Jess … she broke her ankle!

1 Rory *didn't do* the long jump. Rory *swam in the swimming race*.

2 Cassie .... in the swimming race. She ....

3 Delia .... the javelin. She ....

4 Connor .... in the 100-metre race. He ....

5 Jess .... her ankle. She .... three metres in the long jump!

4 Reading and grammar

a) Eva had a busy weekend. Use the words to write questions.

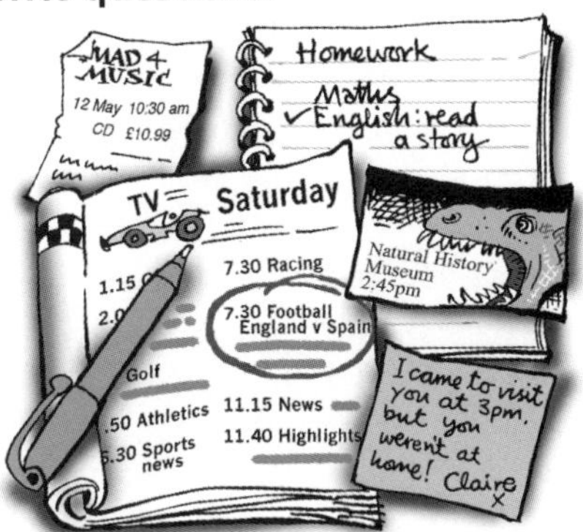

1 What / she / buy *What did she buy* ?

2 What / she / do / in the evening .... ?

3 What museum / she / go to .... ?

4 Who / visit / her .... ?

5 What English homework / she / do .... ?

6 she / do / her Maths homework .... ?

b) Now answer the questions in part a. Use the verbs in the box to write the answers.

didn't read ~~bought~~ went visited watched

1 *She bought a CD.*

2 ....

3 ....

4 ....

5 ....

6 ....

5 Grammar

a) Match the verbs with the nouns.

1 play — f
2 read
3 visit
4 watch
5 get
6 go

a cycling
b a DVD
c music magazines
d a new bike
e my friend
f tennis

b) Complete the text. Use the past simple form of the phrases in part a.

Yesterday was my birthday. I [1] got a new bike. So I [2] .... in the park in the morning. It's a really nice bike. I [3] ...., Lucy, and we [4] .... at the sports centre. I won all our games! Then we went to Lucy's house and [5] .... – it was my birthday present from Lucy. Then we [6] .... and talked about our favourite songs.

6 What were you doing?

1 Vocabulary

a) Look at the picture and complete the crossword.

1 *H A M M O C K*

2

3

4

5

6

b) Unscramble the shaded letters. What singer was Jess listening to?

R ....

2 Reading and grammar

Look at the list. Then look at Activity 1. Complete the sentences.

Weekend jobs in the garden

Cassie – water the flowers

Rory – play with the cat

Connor – mow the lawn

Jess – hang up the washing

1 Cassie *wasn't watering* the flowers.
She *was reading* (read).

2 Rory .... with the cat
He .... (play) on the clothes line.

3 What was the cat doing?
It .... (sleep).

4 Connor .... the lawn
He .... (climb) a tree.

5 Jess .... the washing.
She .... (sit) on the lawn.
She .... (listen) to music.

6 What was the dog doing?
It .... (bury) a bone.

3 Grammar

a) Use the words to write questions.

a Cassie / water / the flowers
Was Cassie watering the flowers

b the boys / play / football
....

c Connor / climb / a tree
....

d Cassie and Connor / look at / the dog
....

b) Match the questions with the answers.

1 Yes, he was. ☐

2 Yes, they were. ☐

3 No, she wasn't. ☐

4 No, they weren't. ☐

4 Grammar and writing

a) Look at Picture A. Use the phrases in the box to complete the sentences.

~~get up~~	have a shower
play football	talk on the phone

At 10 o'clock …

1 Milly *was getting up* .

2 Bob and Jim ....

3 Mum ....

4 Dad ....

b) Now look at Picture B. Find the differences. Use the phrases in the box to write sentences.

hang up the washing	mow the lawn
~~sleep in a hammock~~	play tennis

At 11 o'clock …

1 Milly *wasn't getting up. She was sleeping in a hammock* .

2 Bob and Jim ....

3 Mum ....

4 Dad ....

5 Writing

Write true answers to the questions.

What were you doing at …

1 10.00 on Sunday morning? *I was* ....

2 7.00 this morning? ....

3 8.30 last night? ....

4 midday yesterday? ....

5 3.30pm on Saturday? ....

Module 2

7 Amazing stories

❶ Vocabulary and reading

a) Label the picture. Use the words in the box.

alarm fire saucepan referee ~~smoke~~ [illegible]e

b) Look at the five incorrect words. Write the correct words.

Yesterday we were playing football when we heard a loud noise. It was the [1]**smoke**. But Rick didn't hear anything. He had the ball and he was running towards the goal. The [2]**saucepan** blew his [3]**referee**. We saw smoke. The [4]**whistle** in the kitchen was on [5]**alarm**. 'Run!' shouted the referee. 'I am running!' shouted Rick. Poor Rick! He scored a goal, but the match was over!

1 *alarm* ....
2 ....
3 ....
4 ....
5 ....

❷ Grammar

Look at the pictures and complete the sentences. Use the correct form of the verbs in brackets.

1 He *was walking* .... in the hills when his boot *came off* .... (walk, come off)

2 He .... a shower when he .... the fire alarm. (have, he

3 She .... a comic when she .... into a tree. (read, walk)

4 She .... a story when the pencil .... (write, break)

3 Grammar and reading

Choose the correct words.

STRANGE DRIVER ON MAIN STREET!

Yesterday afternoon two police officers [1] **travel** … on Main Street when they [2] … something very strange. There [3] … a car in front of them. It [4] … very slowly. The police officers [5] … the car when they [6] … that the driver was a dog! It [7] … on its owner's legs. When the police [8] … the car, the owner said, 'Fido [9] … really well! I don't know why you [10] … us.'

travel
see
be
drive
pass
notice
sit
stop
drive
stop

4 Reading and grammar

Read Jo's story. Match the questions with the answers.

One day, my friend and I were shopping. We were walking down the High Street when we saw a new shop with nice, cheap clothes. We were looking at some coats when suddenly I saw a really nice jacket. There was only one, so I tried it on. I was looking at myself in the mirror when a woman asked me, 'Why are you wearing my jacket?' I was so embarrassed!

1 What were Jo and her friend doing in the High Street? [c]
2 Where did they see the nice, cheap clothes? [ ]
3 What were they looking at first? [ ]
4 What did Jo see then? [ ]
5 When did the woman talk to her? [ ]
6 Why was she embarrassed? [ ]

a the coats
b She was wearing the woman's jacket.
c They were shopping.
d in a new shop
e a really nice jacket
f when she was looking at herself in the mirror

5 Writing

Use the prompts to write a story. Use the past simple and the past continuous.

Tom walk to school / he see a letter in the street
he read the letter / it blow away in the wind
he run to catch it / he fall over
he twist his ankle
he rub his foot / the letter land next to him
he read the letter

Tom was walking to school when he saw a letter in the street.

...

The letter said, 'Today is your lucky day!'

8 My hero

1 Reading

a) Read about Rebecca Adlington. Match the questions with the paragraphs.

1 What kind of things does she like? [d]
2 How much training did she do? [ ]
3 Why is she famous? [ ]
4 Where were her parents? [ ]

Rebecca Adlington

a Rebecca Adlington was born on 17th February 1989 in England. She's famous because she broke the world record for the 800-metre freestyle swimming race at the 2008 Beijing Olympic Games. She won two gold medals.
b Rebecca's parents were watching television at home when she won the 400-metre freestyle race. Then they flew to China and watched her second race.
c Rebecca started swimming when she was four. She trained hard for the Olympics. She swam 70 kilometres per week.
d She loves watching TV and buying new shoes! After her races, she wanted to eat a burger and chips!

b) Read again. Correct the sentences.

1 Rebecca broke the world record for the 400-metre freestyle swimming race.
Rebecca broke the world record for the 800-metre freestyle swimming race.

2 Her parents watched her first race in Beijing.
....

3 After her races, she wanted to watch TV.
....

2 Writing

Read the fact file and write about Chris Hoy. Use the text in Activity 1 and the questions below to help you.

When and where was he born? What medals did he win at the Beijing Olympics?
When did he start cycling? Where? What other sports did he do at school? What was his childhood dream

Born: 23rd March 1976, Scotland
Olympic medals: 4 golds, 1 silver (he won three Olympic gold medals at the Beijing Games in 2008)
Career: started cycling at six years old at a friend's house
Other sports when he was at school: rugby, rowing
Chidhood dream: to win an Olympic gold medal

Chris Hoy was born on 23rd March 1976 in Scotland.
....

Module 2 Learning diary

Name .... Date ....

Study tip
Vocabulary

Draw pictures next to new words in your notebook.

fire   fire alarm

Draw pictures for these words.

saucepan   whistle   javelin

Check you can do these things:

1 I know the past simple of verbs. ☐

Write the verbs in the past simple.

1 jump *jumped*
2 twist ....
3 break ....
4 get ....
5 fall ....
6 buy ....

2 I can talk about the past. ☐

Complete the diary. Use the past simple form of the verbs in brackets.

Yesterday was sports day. I [1] ran (run) in a race, but I [2] .... (not swim) in the swimming race. I [3] .... (throw) the javelin and [4] .... (jump) three metres in the long jump. In the afternoon, I [5] .... (do) the obstacle course. I [6] .... (finish) it in eight minutes, but I [7] .... (not break) the record!

3 I can ask and answer questions about the past. ☐

Use the words to write questions and answers in the past simple.

1 What / you / do / yesterday (I / go to an exhibition)
What did you do yesterday ?
I went to an exhibition.

2 Dan / buy / a football (No)
.... ?
....

3 What / you / do / last night (We / watch TV)
.... ?
....

4 What / Sally / eat / for breakfast (She / eat / fruit)
.... ?
....

5 you / read / a book / yesterday (Yes)
.... ?
....

4 I can describe past activities. ☐

Write what everybody was doing on Saturday afternoon.

1 (play) They *were playing* tennis.
2 (climb) He .... a tree.
3 (listen) She .... to music.
4 (ride) We .... our bikes.
5 (do) I .... my homework.

Module 3
Experiences and news

9 In my life

1 Vocabulary

Look at the clues. Complete the crossword.

Down

1 My favourite … star is Beyoncé.
2 A king and a queen often live in a …
3 I like … music, like Jay-Z.
4 
5 At the end of the year, we take … in every subject.
6 I'm studying – we have a big Maths … tomorrow.

Across

7 
8 The highest mountain is … Everest.
9 I don't like this green vegetable.
10 

2 Grammar

a) Write the past participles of the verbs.

1 go *been*
2 climb ....
3 win ....
4 see ....
5 eat ....
6 ride ....
7 travel ....
8 fly ....

b) Complete the sentences. Use the present perfect form of the verbs in brackets.

1 I *'ve been* (be) to England.
2 I .... (ride) an elephant.
3 I .... (fly) across Europe on an aeroplane.
4 I .... (see) the Tower of London.
5 I .... (win) lots of races.
6 I .... (travel) to lots of countries.
7 I .... (climb) the Eiffel Tower.
8 I .... (eat) Italian food.

3 Grammar

Complete Lydia's postcard. Use the correct form of the verbs in the box.

~~taste food from China and Japan~~ ✔ eat Indian sweets ✘ ~~see a magic show~~ ✘ ~~play tennis~~ ✔ ride a horse ✘ dance to hip hop music ✔ listen to stories ✔ jump on a trampoline ✔ win a prize ✘

Hi Mum,

I'm having a great time here at the park today. I've done so many things! I [1] *'ve played* .... tennis, but I [2] *haven't seen* .... a magic show. I [3] .... a horse, but I [4] .... to hip hop music! I [5] .... food from China and Japan, but I [6] .... Indian sweets. I [7] .... to stories and I [8] .... on a trampoline. But I [9] .... a prize ... ☹

Lydia

4 Grammar and reading

Use the words in the box to complete the poem.

stayed ~~flown~~ seen ~~been~~ ~~ridden~~ sailed

I've never [1] *ridden* .... a motorbike,
I've never [2] .... on a ship.
I've never [3] .... in an aeroplane,
And I've never been on a trip. I've never wanted frogs' legs, And I've never [4] .... to Rome. I've never [5] .... the Eiffel Tower, because I've always [6] .... at home!

5 Grammar

a) Use the words to write the questions and short answers.

1 fly to India? ✘ *Have you ever flown to India? No, I haven't.*
2 go to America? ✔ ....
3 travel by train? ✔ ....
4 dance to hip hop? ✘ ....
5 climb a tree? ✔ ....
6 win a prize? ✘ ....

b) Look at Part a and write full sentences.

1 *I've never flown to India.*
2 *I've been to America.*
3 ....
4 ....
5 ....
6 ....

6 Writing

Write about your experiences. Use the questions in the box to help you.

Have you ever been to China? Have you ever climbed a mountain? Have you ever won a race? Have you ever seen a lion?

I've never been to China, but I've been to Australia.

....

10 An amazing life

1 Vocabulary

Match the phrases about Charlotte's life with the pictures.

1 won a swimming race [*e*]
2 ridden an elephant [ ]
3 met a king [ ]
4 written a travel book [ ]

5 climbed Mount Everest [ ]
6 eaten Mexican food [ ]
7 skied in Switzerland [ ]
8 sailed around the world [ ]

2 Grammar

Look at Activity 1 and the words in brackets. Write sentences about Charlotte.

1 (cycling race ✘) *She's won a swimming race, but she hasn't won a cycling race.*

2 (donkey ✘) ....

3 (queen ✘) ....

4 (recipe book ✘) ....

5 (Mont Blanc ✘) ....

6 (Thai food ✘) ....

7 (Canada ✘) ....

8 (from Sydney to Hobart ✘) ....

❸ Reading and Grammar

a) Charlotte wants to do a lot of other things. Read the list.

Things I want to do in my life!
go on holiday to the moon
live in an igloo ✔ 1998
meet the Queen of England
make a film ✔ 1999
swim across the Pacific
fly in a helicopter
cycle to Morocco ✔ last year
break a world record ✔ 2010

b) Complete the questions. Look at the list and write the answers.

1 *Has she been* on holiday to the moon?
No, she hasn't.

2 *Has she lived* in an igloo?
Yes, she has. She lived in an igloo in 1998.

3 .... the Queen of England?
....

4 .... a film?
....
....

5 .... across the Pacific?
....

6 .... in a helicopter?
....

7 .... to Morocco?
....
....

8 .... a world record?
....
....

❹ Grammar

Choose the correct words.

1 Have you ever **been/went** to the desert? (been circled)
2 Yes, I **been/went** two years ago.
3 Have you ever **written/wrote** a story?
4 Yes, I **written/wrote** one last week.
5 Have you ever **eaten/ate** chickens' feet?
6 Yes, I **eaten/ate** them in Peru.
7 Have you ever **swum/swam** in a river?
8 Yes, I **swum/swam** in the Danube last summer.

❺ Writing

Read the notes. Write about Humphrey.

climb Mount Everest ✔
swim across the English Channel ✔
break a leg or an arm ✘
sail to Antarctica ✔
make a TV programme ✘

Humphrey Hill has had an amazing life.
He's climbed Mount Everest.
....
....
....
....
....
....
....
....

Module 3

11 My latest news

1 Vocabulary

Choose the words that go with each verb.

1 change **happy/your hairstyle**
2 find **a new job/a sleepover**
3 buy **an MP3 player/your back**
4 invite **kittens to a sleepover/a friend to a sleepover**
5 paint **your hairstyle/the kitchen**
6 hurt **your back/your sleepover**

2 Vocabulary and grammar

Complete the sentences. Use words from Activity 1.

1 Rory has just hurt his *back*.

2 The cat has just had ....

3 Cassie has just painted the ....

4 Delia has just invited her friend to a ....

5 Jess has just changed her ....

6 Connor has just bought a new ....

3 Grammar

Put the words in the correct order to make sentences.

1 I / bought / just / this new jumper / have
I have just bought this new jumper.

2 has / Mum / a cake / just / made
....

3 he / fallen off / just / has / his bike
....

4 finished / just / they / have / their lesson
....

5 just / we / lunch / have / had
....

6 have / Ben and Vicky / met / just
....

4 Vocabulary and grammar

a) Use the words in the box to complete the sentences.

lunch	a prize	TV	~~shopping~~	a celebrity	a picture

1 I've just been *shopping*. [*d*]
2 I've just won .... [ ]
3 I've just watched .... [ ]
4 I've just met .... [ ]
5 I've just painted .... [ ]
6 I've just eaten .... [ ]

b) Match the questions with the sentences in part a.

a What did you paint?
b Who did you meet?
c What did you win?
d What did you buy?
e What did you eat?
f What did you watch?

5 Grammar

Complete the conversations. Use the correct form of the verbs in brackets.

Ollie: [1] *Have you ever bought* (you / ever / buy) something expensive?
Emma: Yes, I [2] ....
Ollie: What [3] *did you buy?* (you / buy)
Emma: I [4] .... (buy) a digital camera with my birthday money.

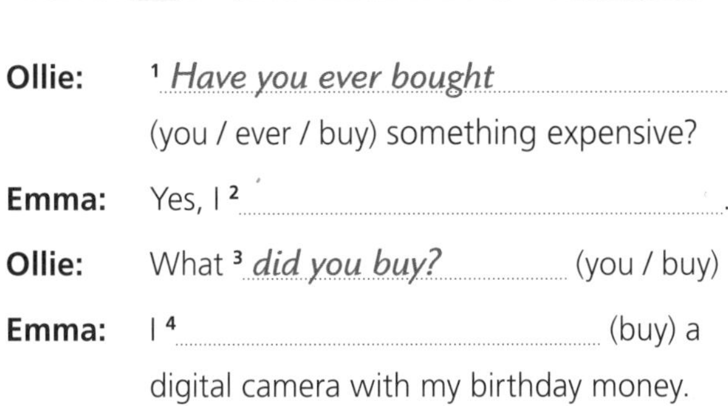

Emma: [5] .... (you / ever / go) skiing?
Ollie: No, [6] ....
Emma: It's really fun.
Ollie: When [7] .... (you / go)?
Emma: We [8] .... (go) last winter.

6 Writing

Write questions for the sentences. Use the words in the box.

When	Who	~~Where~~	What	get	~~go~~	fly	see

1 I've just been on holiday. *Where did you go?*
2 I've just seen someone I know. ....
3 She's just got her birthday present. ....
4 They've just flown to Italy. ....

12 Sumeo's story

1 Reading

a) Read the text and label the pictures. Use the words in the box.

igloo fishing snowmobile ~~Dennis~~

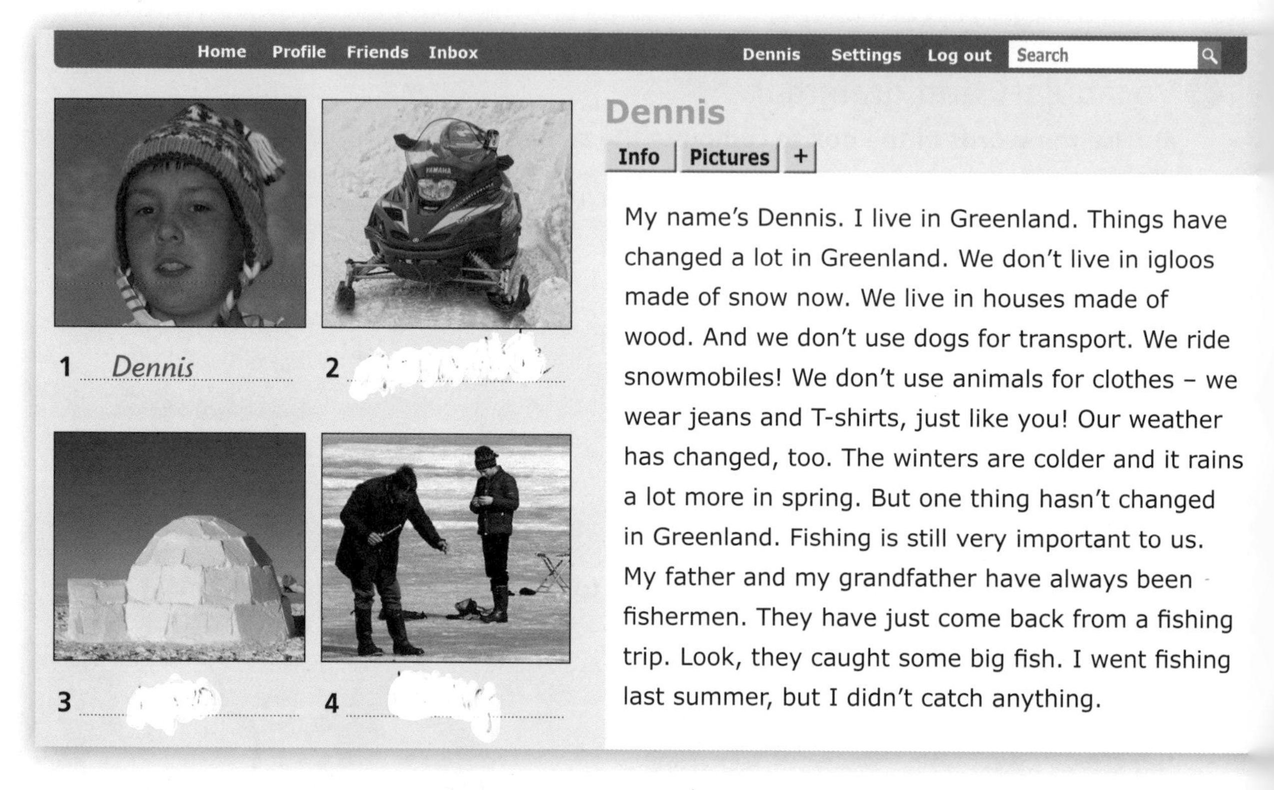

My name's Dennis. I live in Greenland. Things have changed a lot in Greenland. We don't live in igloos made of snow now. We live in houses made of wood. And we don't use dogs for transport. We ride snowmobiles! We don't use animals for clothes – we wear jeans and T-shirts, just like you! Our weather has changed, too. The winters are colder and it rains a lot more in spring. But one thing hasn't changed in Greenland. Fishing is still very important to us. My father and my grandfather have always been fishermen. They have just come back from a fishing trip. Look, they caught some big fish. I went fishing last summer, but I didn't catch anything.

b) Read again. Match the questions with the answers.

1 Where is Dennis from?
2 What were houses made of before?
3 What are houses made of now?
4 What do they use for transport now?
5 What hasn't changed in Greenland?
6 What have Dennis' father and grandfather just done?
7 What did they catch?

a They caught some big fish.
b They drive snowmobiles.
c He's from Greenland.
d They were made of snow.
e They've just been fishing.
f They are made of wood.
g They still go fishing.

2 Writing

Write about where you live. Use the questions in the box to help you.

Do you live in the countryside or a town/city?
Do you live in a house or a flat?
Why?/Why not?
What is your village's/town's/city's name?
Do you like the place where you live?
What kind of things have changed in your town?

I live in the countryside.

Module 3 Learning diary

Name .... Date ....

Study tip
Grammar

Write verb lists in your notebook. Add nouns next to the verbs.

Regular verbs
Present simple/Past simple/Present perfect
I **watch/watched/have watched** TV.
I **climb/climbed/have climbed** a tree.
I play/......................................
....

Irregular verbs
Present simple/Past simple/Present perfect
I **go/went/have been** shopping.
I **see/saw/have seen** a famous person.
....
....

Write the correct form of these verbs in the table and add nouns.

do eat play dance

Check you can do these things:

1 I can talk about experiences. ☐

Write what James has and hasn't done.

1 do his English homework ✔
He has done his English homework.

2 finish his book ✘
....

3 start his project ✔
....

4 write a poem ✘
....

2 I can ask and answer about experiences. ☐
Use the words to write questions and answers.

1 you / ever / be to Germany
Have you ever been to Germany?
Yes, *I have*. When *did you go*?
I went in 2007.

2 your dad / ever / play football
....?
No, ...

3 your parents / ever / meet an athlete
....?
Yes, ... Who ....?
.... Usain Bolt.

3 I can talk about recent news. ☐
Write what has just happened. Use the correct form of the verbs in brackets.

1 The girl *has just fallen off* (fall off) her horse.

2 Arsenal .... (win) the match.

3 They .... (arrive) in Argentina.

Module 4
Dancing, acting, singing

13 The talent show

1 Vocabulary

Find six words in the wordsnake. Use the words to label the picture.

2 Vocabulary and grammar

Look at Activity 1. Complete the sentences. Use *will* (✔) or *won't* (✘).

1 Delia *will* .... fall off the stage. ✔
2 She .... hurt the girl in the audience. ✘
3 Jess .... kick the microphone. ✔
4 Rory .... drop the microphone. ✔
5 The audience .... hear him singing. ✘
6 They .... win first prize. ✘
7 The audience .... laugh at them. ✔

3 Vocabulary and grammar

a) Label the pictures. Use the words in th box.

sing act play the guitar do a magic trick da

1 *dance*
2 ....
3 ....
4 ....
5 ....

b) **Look at the chart. Choose the correct words.**

Talent Show!

Do you want to dance, sing or act? Do you want to play the guitar or do a magic trick?

Write your name here!

sing	act	play guitar	do a magic trick	dance
Liz	Lou	Dexter	Tina, Simon	Lou, Liz, Dexter, Tina, Simon

Teacher: Good morning, class! Now, let's talk about the talent show.
Lou: I [1] **'ll/won't** act. I've practised a sketch.
Teacher: OK! What about you, Dexter? What [2] **will/won't** you do?
Dexter: I [3] **'ll/won't** play the guitar.
Teacher: Will you sing, too?
Dexter: No, I [4] **will/won't**. But Liz has got a great voice. She [5] **'ll/won't** sing.
Teacher: Right. Who [6] **will/won't** do a magic trick?
Simon: Tina [7] **will/won't** do a magic trick.
Tina: Yes, I [8] **will/won't**. And Simon [9] **will/won't** help me.
Liz: And we [10] **'ll/won't** all dance to a hip hop song!
Teacher: Great! I can't wait for the show!

4 Grammar

Match to make sentences.

1	Claude will	a	a good teacher.
2	I won't live	b	amazing invention.
3	One day, Sonja will be	c	first prize.
4	We won't travel	d	in a big house.
5	I think Jess will win	e	meet a celebrity.
6	The teacher will ask	f	to China.
7	The pilot	g	will fly a plane.
8	They will design an	h	you a question.

5 Grammar

Complete the sentences with *'ll*, *will* or *won't*.

A: Will it rain tomorrow?
B: No, it [1] *won't*. Look. The sky is blue. It [2] ______ be a nice day tomorrow.

A: Will there be any famous people at the show?
B: Yes, there [3] ______.

A: How many children will you have in the future?
B: I think I [4] ______ have six children!

A: Will you live in a different country one day?
No, I [5] ______. But I [6] ______ live in this city. I [7] ______ move to a farm.

A: What amazing invention will they design in the future?
B: I think they [8] ______ invent a new kind of car – a car that can fly!

6 Writing

Write predictions about your future. Use the questions to help you.

Will you be famous?
What job will you do?
Will you live in a different country?
Will you live in a city or in the countryside?
Will you have children? How many?

I won't be famous. I'll be a police officer.

14 Helpful Herbert

1 Vocabulary

Look at the pictures and unscramble the words.

1

lionvi *violin*

2

pam ....

3

oncoracdi ....

4
edblou sabs ....

5

smurd ....

6
rcreoedr ....

7
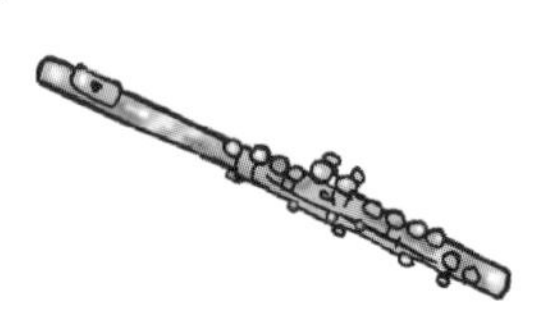
lutef ....

8

srkodyeba ....

2 Grammar and vocabulary

a) Match the sentences with the pictures.

1 I'm cold.
2 I'm hungry.
3 I can't do this homework.
4 I've lost my glove.
5 I can't hear the music.
6 I'm thirsty.

b) Match the sentences in part a with the requests below.

a Could you help me with it, please? [3]
b Can you close the window, please? [ ]
c Can you look for it, please? [ ]
d Can you buy me some crisps, please? [ ]
e Can I have a drink of water, please? [ ]
f Could you turn up the volume, please? [ ]

3 Grammar

Read the problems and write offers. Use the phrases in the box.

show you on a map take it away get you a cold drink ~~carry your bags for you~~

1 I've hurt my back.
I'll carry your bags for you.

2 There's a spider on my desk!
....

3 I'm hot.
....

4 I don't know where your house is.
....

4 Grammar

Choose the correct words.

1 Could (**I**)/**you** borrow your pencil, please?
2 Could **I/you** lend me some money?
3 Could **I/you** use your dictionary for a moment?
4 Can you **lend/borrow** me your phone, please?
5 Could **I/you** fix my computer, please?
6 Can I **lend/borrow** this DVD from you?

5 Grammar

Read the problems. Use the words to write requests.

1 I've lost my calculator. (borrow / yours)
Could I borrow yours, please?
2 My computer's broken. (fix / it)
..........?
3 I don't know this word. (use / your dictionary)
..........?
4 My head hurts. (have / an aspirin)
..........?
5 I don't know where the shop is. (tell / me)
..........?

6 Writing and grammar

Read the problems and write offers. Use the phrases in the box to help you.

~~lend you some money~~ explain it to you look for it turn on the TV lend you some clothes

1 I haven't got any money.
I'll lend you some money.
2 I can't find my necklace.
....
3 My clothes are wet.
....
4 I don't understand.
....
5 I'm bored.
....

15 The festival

1 Vocabulary

Label the posters. Use the words in the box.

street dance | mime | comedy show | circus | ~~puppet show~~ | folk music

a *puppet show* ....
b ....
c ....

You won't believe what they can do!!
Come and see for yourself on High Street at 2.30!

d ....
e ....
f ....

2 Vocabulary and reading

Read the descriptions. Match them with the shows in Activity 1.

1 Olga is a dancer. She dances to hip hop music outside in the park. [*f*]
2 There are three people in this band. They play the violin, the recorder and the guitar. [ ]
3 This person is an actor. But he doesn't talk at all in his shows. [ ]
4 Hilary works with dolls on strings. They move just like real people! [ ]
5 Brendan tells funny stories. The audiences laugh a lot in his shows. [ ]

3 Grammar

Choose the correct words.

1 How about **going**/**to go** to the theatre tonight? (*going* circled)
2 Let's **to watch/watch** a puppet show.
3 I'd like **seeing/to see** something funny.
4 I don't want **listening/to listen** to jazz.
5 What would you like **to do/doing**?
6 **I want to/How about** see a play.
7 Would you like **go out/to go out** tonight?

❹ Grammar

Put the words in the correct order to make questions and sentences.

1 you / do / like / tonight / what / would / to *What would you like to do tonight* ?
2 want / don't / I / to / dance ....
3 theatre / about / going / how / the / to .... ?
4 a / let's / game / play ....

❺ Grammar and reading

a) Number the parts of the conversation in the correct order.

a ☐ **Emma:** A puppet show? No way! How about [1] *having* (have) something to eat at a restaurant?

b [8] **Emma:** Good idea! Let's [2] .... (do) that. I want a pizza with cheese and spinach. What about you?

c ☐ **Emma:** Let's [3] .... (walk) to the park. There's a rock band playing there tonight.

d ☐ **Emma:** Oh, no. I hate folk music. I [4] .... (not want) to listen to that! Let's [5] .... (watch) some mime.

e ☐ **Ollie:** I [6] .... (not like) mime. It's boring. I'd like to [7] .... (see) a puppet show.

f ☐ **Ollie:** I think that will be too noisy. How about [8] .... (listen) to some folk music?

g ☐ **Ollie:** OK, there's a comedy show at the Pizza Place tonight. How about [9] .... (go) there and [10] .... (watch) a comedy show while we eat?

h [1] **Ollie:** What would you like to [11] .... (do) tonight, Em?

b) Complete the conversation. Use the correct form of the verbs in brackets.

❻ Writing

Write about things to do on holiday. Use the phrases in the box and your own ideas.

do homework	learn a language	tidy your room	go to a circus
listen to opera	watch DVDs	go swimming	

I don't want to do homework! I'd like to go swimming.

16 The Brit School

1 Reading

a) Read the article. Would you like to go to this school?

These students go to a performing arts school in England. They all want to be famous actors, singers or dancers when they finish school. At this school, they study English, Maths, Science, French, History and Art, but they also study Drama and Dance.

JACK
I love this school. But it isn't just fun all the time. It's hard work. We have the same homework as other school children, but we also have to practise drama and music and dancing – even when we are tired! Right now, I'd really like to go to bed and sleep, but I've got a singing lesson.

BETH
I've been in five shows. I like acting and singing, but my favourite subject is Dance and that's what I want to do when I'm older. At the moment, we are practising for a big street dance festival. I think we'll win – we're very good!

AIDEN
At the moment, in Theatre Studies, we're learning about stage design. There's a lot to think about! Will the audience see everything? How will the actors come on to the stage? Where will the microphones be? It's interesting. I'd like to have a job in the theatre one day.

b) Read again. Answer the questions.

1 Who wants to work in the theatre? *Aiden*
2 Who wants to be a dancer? ....
3 Who would like to have a rest? ....
4 Who has to go to a singing lesson? ....
5 Who is studying stage design? ....
6 Who is going to dance in a festival? ....

2 Writing

Look at the poster. Make your own poster for a sports event. Use the phrases in the box.

Would you like to …? Do you want to …? How about …? There'll be … You'll … You won't …

WOULD YOU LIKE TO WATCH AN AMAZING SHOW?

There'll be magic tricks, mime, comedy, singing and the best street dancing you've ever seen!

You'll love it. You won't see a better show in your life!

Module 4 Learning diary

Name .... Date ....

Study tip

Writing – punctuation

Remember to use the apostrophe (') for contractions. It shows that there is a letter or letters missing.

we will = we'll there is = there's

Write the contractions.

I am *I'm*
they will ....
you will not ....
let us ....
I would ....

Check you can do these things:

1 I know words for musical instruments. ☐

Complete the words.

1 r*ecorder*
2 f..........
3 k..........
4 a..........

2 I know words about shows. ☐

Write the words under the definitions.

audience microphone ~~mime~~ stage

1 a performance without speaking
mime
2 the people watching a performance
....
3 you speak into this to make your voice louder
....
4 you stand on this when you are acting
....

3 I can ask about and make predictions. ☐

Complete the questions and answers. Use *will* or *won't*.

1 *Will* I be rich one day?
No, you ....
2 .... Cathy marry a pop star?
Yes, she ....
3 .... they travel to a distant country?
No, they ....

4 I can make polite requests. ☐

Rewrite the instructions as requests.

1 Open the window!
Could you open the window, please?
2 Get my coat!
....
3 Lend me your pencil!
....
4 Buy me a drink!
....

5 I can make offers. ☐

Use the phrases to write offers.

1 turn up the radio
I'll turn up the radio.
2 show you the way
....
3 buy you a ticket
....
4 fix your bike
....

Module 5
Good advice

17 How are you feeling?

1 Vocabulary

Look the pictures. Complete the sentences about Connor. Use the words in the box.

a cold	a headache	medicine	flu	~~a sore throat~~	a stomach ache	temperature	a cough

1 On Monday, he had *a sore throat*.
2 On Tuesday, he had ....
3 On Wednesday, he had ....
4 On Thursday, he had ....
5 On Friday, he had a very high ....
6 On Saturday, he had ....
7 On Sunday, he had .... The doctor gave him some .... to take.

2 Vocabulary

Choose the correct words.

1 Cover your mouth when you **cold/cough**.
2 Don't eat too many sweets. You'll get a **stomach ache/headache**.
3 Don't go to school when you've got a **cold/better**.
4 Don't read in a dark room. You'll get **flu/a headache**.
5 Don't shout too much at the concert. You'll get a **temperature/sore throat**.
6 Take your **temperature/medicine**. Then you'll feel better.

3 Grammar

Find the mistakes. Write the correct words.

1 If you go to bed earlier, you will be tired in the morning. *won't*
2 If you carries that heavy bag, you'll hurt your back. ....
3 If you take an aspirin, it is helping your headache. ....
4 If you study hard, you will fail the test. ....
5 If you are writing things down, you'll remember them better. ....
6 If you don't hurry up, you are missing the bus. ....

4 Grammar

Look at the pictures. Use the words to write sentences.

1 she / ride her bike too fast / she / fall
If she rides her bike too fast, she'll fall.

2 they / eat too many sweets / they / get a stomach ache

3 he / not wear warm clothes / he / get ill

4 he / not study harder / he / fail his test

5 Polly / not tidy her room / her mum / be angry

6 he / eat a lot of fruit / he / be healthy

5 Writing

Complete the sentences for you. Use the phrases in the box.

invite me to their houses	not miss the bus	not let me go out	share their things with me
be unhealthy	put on weight	get a stomach ache	get a place at university
buy a book/an MP3 player/a CD/some jeans, etc.	be on time for school	get my allowance	

1 If I don't listen to my parents, *they won't let me go out*.
2 If I do well at school, .
3 If I am nice to my friends, .
4 If I don't do any exercise, .
5 If I eat too much chocolate, .
6 If I save my allowance, .
7 If I do my chores, .
8 If I get up on time, .

18 I'm worried

❶ Vocabulary

Look at the pictures and unscramble the words.

1 mawr tesclho
warm clothes

2 nett
....

3 cstein arsyp
....

4 ameg
....

5 lulb
....

❷ Grammar

Look at the pictures. Complete Delia's sentences with *may* or *may not* and the words in the bo

be sleep fall like ~~lose~~ rain

1 I *may lose* .... all my money.
2 I .... because I'm scared.
3 There .... snakes.
4 It .... on the tent.
5 I .... into the water.
6 I .... the food.

3 Grammar and reading

Look at the chart and complete the sentences. Use *going to*.

ACTIVITY CAMP

Which activities are you going to do?

go for a walk	Cassie
play beach volleyball	Jess, Delia, Rory
make a video	Connor, Jess
have a barbeque	Delia, Cassie, Connor
run a race	Rory
swim to the island	

1 Cassie *is going to* go for a walk.
2 Connor *isn't going to* go for a walk. He .... make a video with Jess.
3 Three people .... play beach volleyball.
4 Connor, Delia and Cassie .... run a race. They .... have a barbeque.
5 Rory .... run a race.
6 But no-one .... swim to the island!

4 Grammar

Choose the correct words.

Emma: What [1] **may you/are you** going to do this weekend?
Ollie: I'm not sure. I [2] **may/'m going to** go shopping, or I [3] **may/'m going to** just hang out with my friends at home. What about you?
Emma: I [4] **may/'m going to** see a film at the cinema. I've already got a ticket.
Ollie: What film [5] **may you/are you going to** see?
Emma: I don't know.
Ollie: But you've got a ticket already!
Emma: It's a free ticket. I can see any film I want. I [6] **may/'m going to** see a scary film or I [7] **may/'m going to** choose a comedy. I'll see when I get to the cinema!

5 Writing

Write about your plans for the weekend. Use the pictures to help you.

I'm going to *watch a DVD with my family*.

I may ....

If ...., I'll ....

I'm not going to ....

I may not ....

19 You should say thank you

1 Vocabulary

a) Match the words and pictures with the definitions.

1  wet [a]

2  muddy [ ]

3  visitors [ ]

4  present [ ]

5  take off [ ]

6  rude [ ]

7  stare [ ]

a not dry

b stop wearing

c not polite

d something you give to someone

e dirty with wet earth

f look at something or someone for a long time

g people who come to see you

b) Complete the sentences. Use the words from part a.

1 You shouldn't go outside with *wet* .... hair. You could get a cold.

2 You shouldn't wear .... boots inside the house.

3 You shouldn't .... at people who look different.

4 When .... come to your house, you should invite them inside.

5 You should .... your hat when you sit down at the table to eat.

6 When someone gives you a ...., you should say thank you.

7 You shouldn't talk with your mouth full of food. It's ....

2 Reading and grammar

Read about customs in China. Choose the correct words.

When it's New Year in China, we have a big festival. But there are lots of jobs to do before New Year's Day. You [1] **should/shouldn't** always clean your house. But you [2] **should/shouldn't** carry the dirt outside through the front door. If you do that, you'll have bad luck. You [3] **should/shouldn't** take the dirt outside through the back door! You [4] **should/shouldn't** wash your hair before New Year. You [5] **should/shouldn't** wash it on New Year's Day – that's too late. For Chinese people, red is a lucky colour, so you [6] **should/shouldn't** wear red clothes and you [7] **should/shouldn't** put red things in your house. You [8] **should/shouldn't** use bad words on New Year's Day – that's also unlucky.

And we also [9] **should/shouldn't** cry! Chinese people say, 'If you cry on New Year's Day, you'll cry the whole year.' I always say to my mother, 'Remember, you [10] **should/shouldn't** shout at me, because then I will cry and I won't stop crying for a year!'

3 Grammar

Match the problems with the advice.

1 I'm getting fat! — e
2 I can't remember my English vocabulary.
3 I can't read the words on the board.
4 I can't find my MP3 player.
5 I get worried about exams.
6 I don't know what to give my mother for her birthday.

a You should make a study timetable.
b You should write the new words in a notebook.
c You should put it in the same place every day.
d You should make her a card.
e You shouldn't eat so many sweets.
f You should wear glasses.

4 Grammar

Look at the pictures and complete the sentences. Use *should* or *shouldn't*.

1 In Malaysia, you *should* .... touch things at the table with your left hand.

2 In Thailand, you .... show the bottom of your feet to anyone.

3 In Britain, you .... put your elbows on the table when you are eating.

4 In Finland, you .... talk with your hands in your pockets.

5 In Japan, you .... blow your nose at the table.

5 Reading and writing

Read the problem and write some advice. Use *should, shouldn't* and the words in the box.

sugar	sweets	fruit	gym
exercise	run	walk	go

It's our school Sports day soon. I want to get fitter. I want to come first in all the events! But I'm quite lazy and I love pizza, chocolate and ice cream! What advice can you give me about food and exercise?

You should eat more fruit.

....

....

....

....

....

....

....

....

....

....

....

20 Survival

1 Reading

a) Read about fire safety. Do you know what to do in a fire?

Fires are very dangerous. If you follow this advice, there won't be fires in your home. And if there is a fire, you'll know what to do!

■ Be careful when you are cooking. You shouldn't hold a towel too close to the cooker. If you do, it will start burning.

■ You shouldn't stand too close to a firework. If you do, you'll burn yourself.

■ You shouldn't go too close to a candle. If you do, your hair or your clothes will start burning.

■ You shouldn't put water on a cooker fire. You should turn off the cooker and wait for the fire to go out.

■ You shouldn't try to blow out a fire in your home. If you do, the fire will get bigger. You should cover the fire with a blanket or a wet cloth and phone the fire brigade immediately.

b) Read again. Are the sentences true (T) or false (F)?

1 You should always hold a towel close to the cooker. *F*
2 You shouldn't put water on a cooker fire. ....
3 You shouldn't turn off the cooker if it is on fire. ....
4 You should stay away from candles. ....
5 You should blow out a fire. ....
6 If you put a wet cloth on the fire, the fire will stop burning. ....

2 Writing

Write advice for a new student at your school. Use the words and phrases in the box.

You should/shouldn't ...	If you ..., you will/won't ...	join after-school clubs					
talk	run	do sport	do homework	eat lunch	sit	walk	stand

You should join after-school clubs.
....
....
....
....
....

Module 5 Learning diary

Name .... Date ....

Study tip
Writing – punctuation

Remember the rules about capital letters! We always use a capital:

- for the first word of a sentence
- for countries, nationalities and languages
- for names of people and places, e.g. rivers, mountains, streets
- for days of the week and months of the year.

Rewrite these sentences with capital letters in the correct places.

mrs brunel, my french teacher, is from paris. *Mrs Brunel,* ....
i live in king street, near the river cam. ....
there's a party on the first sunday in june. ....

Check you can do these things:

1 I know words about illness. ☐

Complete the sentences.

1 When your head hurts, you have a *headache* .
2 When you are ill, you take ....
3 When you have flu, you have a high ....
4 When you shout a lot, you get a ....

2 I can talk about future possibilities. ☐

Match to make sentences.

1 If you don't wear a hat, [*b*]
2 If you get up late for school, ☐
3 You won't get better ☐
4 You'll do well ☐
5 We won't go swimming ☐

a if you study hard.
b your head will burn in the sun.
c if it's cold.
d if you don't stay in bed today.
e you'll miss the bus.

3 I can talk about possible events. ☐

Read the questions. Use the words and *may (not)* to write the answers.

1 Why are you wearing a raincoat? (it / rain)
It may rain ....
2 Why have you made a vegetarian meal? (they / eat / meat)
....
3 Why are you taking insect spray to the beach? (there / be / flies)
....
4 Why are you running? (I / miss / the bus)
....

4 I can give advice. ☐

Read the problems and complete the advice. Use *should* or *shouldn't* .

1 I want to make new friends.
You *should* .... join an after-school club.
2 I can't wake up in the morning!
You .... go to bed so late.
3 I can't do my homework.
You .... ask the teacher for help.
4 My best friend isn't talking to me.
You .... ask him what's wrong.

Module 6
House and home

21 DIY disasters

1 Vocabulary

a) Look at the picture. Complete the crossword.

b) Use the shaded letters. What colour is the wall going to be? *w* ....

2 Vocabulary and grammar

Complete the sentences with words from Activity 1.

1. Jess is going to spill the *paint*.
2. Connor is going to trip over the ....
3. He's going to drop the ....
4. Jess is going to fall off the ....
5. She's going to drop the ....
6. The hammer is going to break the ....

3 Vocabulary

Choose the correct words.

1. Don't jump on the bed – you're going to **spill/break** it. (break circled)
2. Don't run with your drink – you're going to **spill/trip over** it.
3. I can't walk on the wall – I'm scared that I'm going to **fall off/drop** it.
4. I didn't see the stone in the road and I **fell off/tripped over** it.
5. I've lost my keys. I think I **fell off/dropped** them in the park.

4 Grammar

Look at the picture. Use the words and *going to* to write predictions.

1 The waiter / spill / the drink
The waiter is going to spill the drink.
2 The child / trip over / the bag
....
3 The woman / give her friend / a present
....
4 The plates / fall off / the table
....
5 The man / pay / the bill
....

5 Grammar

What are you going to do tonight? Write true answers for you.

Yes, I am / he is / she is / we are / they are.
No, I'm not / he isn't / she isn't / we're not / they're not.

1 You're going to run a marathon.
No, I'm not.
2 You and your friend are going to read.
....
3 Your parents are going to watch TV.
....
4 You're going to call your friend.
....
5 Your friend is going to play football.
....
6 You and your family are going to eat dinner.
....

6 Grammar

a) **Number the pictures in the correct order.**

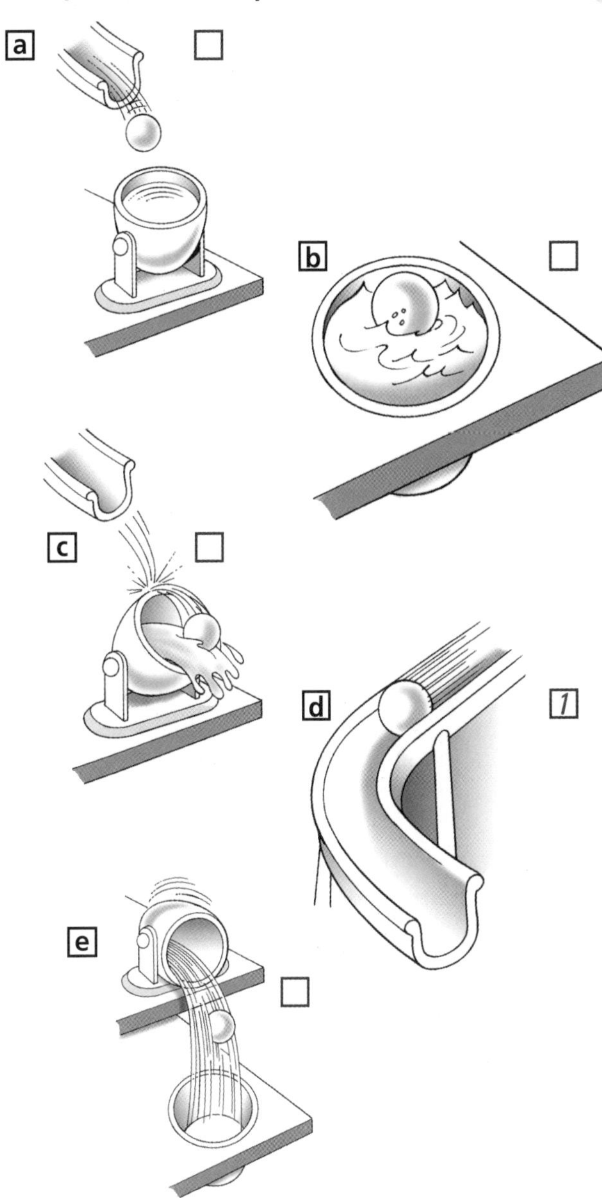

b) **Look at the pictures again and complete the predictions. Use *going to* and the verbs in the box.**

drop fall over float spill ~~travel~~

1 First, the ball *is going to travel* along the 'road'.
2 Then it .... down into the cup.
3 Next, the cup ....
4 The water in the cup .... The water is going to fill the hole.
5 When the hole is full of water, the ball .... on the water.

22 My home

1 Vocabulary

Look at the clues and write the words. Find the words in the word grid.

T	O	U	R	I	S	T	P	Z	R
R	C	E	T	O	U	Y	H	G	L
A	O	C	A	R	A	V	A	N	I
F	U	R	N	I	T	U	R	E	G
F	O	S	W	M	L	T	J	I	H
I	D	F	T	P	O	Z	J	O	T
C	O	T	T	A	G	E	E	G	H
R	A	N	C	H	I	O	K	X	O
S	T	L	C	M	P	R	F	K	U
U	V	C	I	W	T	Y	S	Q	S
E	L	G	A	N	P	J	S	B	E
W	Q	J	W	R	E	S	L	R	J

1 *traffic*

2 a person on holiday in a different country ....

3 a house with a light for ships to see ....

4 ....

5 ....

6 a small house in the countryside ....

7 ....

8 the things you find in a house (sofa, chairs, table) ....

2 Grammar

Are the nouns countable (C) or uncountable (U)?

1 traffic *U*
2 money ......
3 homework ......
4 friend ......
5 space ......
6 time ......
7 book ......
8 song ......

3 Grammar

Complete the sentences. Use *enough*, *too much/many* and words from Activity 2.

1 John's a bit lonely. He's new to the school and he doesn't have *enough friends* yet.

2 Those jeans are expensive. If you buy them, you won't have .... to buy the T-shirt.

3 I can't go to the book shop! I've got .... at home already.

4 The bus took a long time to get to school today, because there was .... on the roads.

5 I don't have time to listen to all the music on my MP3 player. I've got .... on it.

6 I want a sofa in my room, but my room is too small. There just isn't ....

7 I can't go out tonight. I've got .... to do.

8 We can't have a meal before we go to the cinema. We won't have .... to do both things.

❹ Grammar

Rewrite the sentences. Use *not enough* and the adjectives in brackets.

1 Class, you *aren't quiet enough*. (quiet)

2 We can't go swimming today. It .... (warm)

3 You can't drive. You .... (old)

4 This jacket .... (big)

5 Your marks this term .... (good)

6 Sorry, you can't go on this ride. You .... (tall)

❺ Grammar and reading

Read the situations and complete the sentences. Use *not enough* or *too much/many*.

1 There are ten people and eight chairs.
There *aren't enough* chairs.

2 This pizza tastes very salty.
There .... salt on the pizza.

3 There are six of us, but we only have two sandwiches.
There .... food.

4 This cake isn't nice. It needs more sugar.
There .... sugar in the cake.

5 The clothes won't all fit in the wardrobe.
There .... clothes.

❻ Writing

Write about the place you would not like to live. Use *not enough, too much/many* and the words in the box.

noisy quiet interesting exciting cheap expensive people traffic noise mud cars wildlife flowers trees

I would not like to live in the city, because there *are too many people.*
....
....
....

I would not like to live in the countryside, because it's *not exciting enough.*
....
....
....

Module 6

23 The eco-village

1 Reading and vocabulary

Look at the pictures and complete the text. Use the words in the box.

farm	food	kitchen	laundry	recycled	~~village~~	wind turbines

Hillrise is a very special [1] *village* .... Here, we try to be as green as possible. For example, we all live in our own houses, but we share one big [2] .... and we have one shared room for all our [3] ...., too. We have our own small gardens, but we also have a [4] .... We get most of our [5] .... from here – we only buy things we can't grow from the supermarket. We produce our own electricity from [6] .... and all our rubbish is [7] .... We have bins fo paper, glass and plastic.

2 Vocabulary

Match the numbers with the words.

1 2,000 kilos — c
2 2%
3 2.5
4 2,000 000
5 2,000 000 000

a two per cent
b two billion
c two tonnes
d two million
e two point five/ two and a half

3 Grammar

Match to make sentences.

1 Rubbish [c]
2 Every year, trees [ ]
3 Plastic bottles [ ]
4 A lot of rice [ ]
5 Some furniture [ ]
6 Glass [ ]

a is made from melted sand.
b is grown in India.
c is collected in big recycling bins.
d is built from recycled wood.
e are cut down in forests.
f are melted to make fleece.

4 Grammar

Find the past participles of these verbs in the word grid.

1 dry
2 melt
3 sell
4 collect
5 wash
6 use
7 make
8 cut

Q	G	(D	R	I	E	D)	S	A	K
Z	X	C	W	V	B	N	M	L	K
C	J	H	G	A	U	F	D	S	A
O	Q	W	E	R	S	T	Y	U	I
L	O	P	Z	X	E	H	M	C	V
L	B	S	N	M	D	L	E	K	M
E	J	H	O	G	F	D	L	D	A
C	A	W	E	L	R	T	T	Y	D
T	U	I	O	P	D	X	E	C	E
E	V	B	C	U	T	N	D	M	K
D	J	H	G	F	D	S	O	I	U

5 Grammar

Complete the text. Use the passive form of the verbs in brackets.

Recycled Bush Wire Radio –

BUY ONE TODAY!

This amazing eco-friendly radio [1] *is made* .... (make) mainly from old drinks cans. The cans [2] .... (collect) in and around Cape Town, South Africa. The cans [3] .... (wash) and then they [4] .... (dry). Finally, they [5] .... (cut) into pieces and they [6] .... (use) to make this wonderful product. Some of the cans [7] .... (melt) to make different parts of the radio. The radio [8] .... (sell) with a battery, so you can listen to your radio wherever you are!

6 Reading and grammar

a) Complete the text. Use the passive form of the verbs in the box.

dry ~~make~~ use wash put

Did you know you can recycle old crisp packets and make some cool new things? These table mats [1] *are made* .... from old crisp packets. First, the empty crisp packets [2] .... in water and they [3] .... in the sun. Then they [4] .... around long thin sticks. String [5] .... to hold the sticks together.

b) Match the answers from Part a with the pictures below.

a ☐ b ☐ c ☐ d 2

7 Writing

Write about recycling in your home or school. Use the words in the box to help you.

paper glass plastic bottles drinks cans crisp packets bin clothes pens and pencils shoes furniture phones

What is recycled in your home or school?

At our school, paper is recycled.

....

Where are things collected? *Paper is collected in a bin outside each classroom.*

....

Do you use any recycled things in your home? What things?

I often buy recycled clothes.

....

24 The eco-family

❶ Reading

a) Read about an eco-farm. Would you like to live here?

Brithdir Mawr is a farm in Wales. Eight adults and four children live here. Some of the adults have part-time jobs in the town, but everyone has jobs to do in the house, in the vegetable garden or with the animals. Two of the children go to the local primary school and the other two are in college.

Each person or family has their own private space in the farm house, or in one of the farm buildings near the house. The living spaces have their own kitchen, living room and bedrooms, but the bathrooms are shared.

Downstairs in the 'big house', everyone eats together three or four times a week. They grow their own fruit and vegetables on the farm and meals often include milk, eggs, and cheese or yoghurt which come from their own goats and chickens.

The community wants to help the environment so the wind, sun and rain are used to produce energy for electricity. Houses are heated by wood and as much rubbish as possible is recycled.

If you want to learn more about life at *Brithdir Mawr*, you can visit their website.

b) Read again. Answer the questions.

1 How many people live at Brithdir Mawr?
12 people live at Brithdir Mawr.

2 Which rooms are shared?
....

3 How often do they eat together?
....

4 What food is produced on the farm?
....

5 How is energy produced?
....

6 How can you learn more about the farm?
....

❷ Writing

a) Write questions to ask a child from *Brithdir Mawr*. Use the notes and examples to help you.

Lessons: When/have? Where/have? What subjects/study?
Free time: What/do? How often/do?
Jobs: What/do? How often/do? What/favourite/least favourite?
Sharing things: What/share? like/sharing?
General: What/best/worst thing?

Examples: *When do you have lessons? What is your favourite job? Do you like sharing things?*

1 ....?
2 ....?
3 ....
4 ....

b) Imagine you are the child from *Brithdir Mawr*. Write answers to the questions in part a.

1 ....
2 ....
3 ....
4 ....

Module 6 Learning diary

Name .... Date ....

Study tip
Writing – punctuation

Remember these punctuation rules.

Use a question mark (?) at the end of a question.
Use a comma (,) to separate items in a list.
Use an exclamation mark (!) to show feeling.
In all other cases, use a full stop (.).

Punctuate these sentences.

Come here*!*
Do you like ice cream
My favourite kinds of music are rock pop and hip hop

Check you can do these things:

1 I know words about DIY. ☐

Complete the words.

1 l*adder* ....
2 h..........
3 p..........
4 w..........
5 d..........

2 I can make predictions. ☐

Use the words to write predictions.

1 It / rain *It's going to rain* ....
2 He / drop / that box ....
3 He / fall off / his bike ....
4 I / fall asleep soon ....

3 I can talk about quantity. ☐

Complete the sentences. Use *enough* or *too much/many*.

1 I can't buy this CD. I haven't got *enough* money.
2 It's not warm .... in here. I'm cold.
3 We won't get tickets for the show. There are .... people here already.
4 I can't eat all that food! It's .... for me.

4 I can talk about numbers. ☐

Write the numbers in words.

1 100 *one/a hundred*
2 10% ....
3 4.5 ....
4 1,000 000 000 ....

5 I can talk about processes. ☐

Complete the sentences. Use the passive form of the verbs in brackets.

1 In the USA, 85,000,000 tonnes of paper *are used* (use) every year.
2 500,000 trees .... (cut) down to produce Sunday newspapers every week.
3 Every month, enough glass .... (throw) away to fill a giant skyscraper!
4 Plastic bottles .... (recycle) to make fleece.

Module 7
Travelling

25 Rules of the road

1 Vocabulary

a) Match the pictures with the sentences.

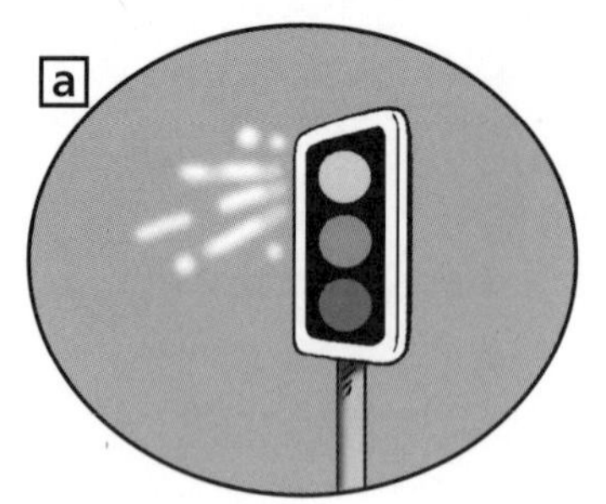
a traffic lights

b ....

c ....

1 Cars drive here. [b]
2 It's got two wheels. [ ]
3 People walk on this part of a street. [ ]
4 These have red, orange and green lights. [ ]
5 You can park here. [ ]
6 You wear it to protect your head. [ ]

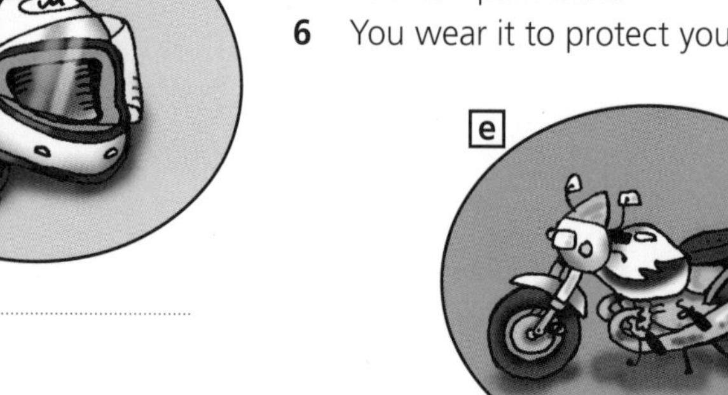
f ....

e ....

d ....

b) Label the pictures in part a. Use the words in the box.

crash helmet ~~traffic lights~~ motorbike pavement road car park

2 Grammar

Complete the sentences. Use *must* or *mustn't*.

1 Don't eat or drink in the street.
You *mustn't* eat or drink in the street.
2 Drive on the left.
You .... drive on the left.
3 Don't run in the classroom.
You .... run in the classroom.
4 Switch off your phone.
You .... switch off your phone.
5 Listen carefully.
You .... listen carefully.
6 Don't walk when the light is red.
You .... walk when the light is red.

3 Grammar

Put the words in the correct order to make sentences.

1 must / you / straight / keep / on
You must keep straight on
2 cross / you / the / mustn't / road
....
3 cycle / mustn't / the / you / on / pavement
....
4 fast / too / you / drive / mustn't
....
5 turn / you / must / here
....
6 bicycles / cycle lane / must / the / use
....

4 Vocabulary

Label the items in the picture. Use the words in the box.

crossroads   cycle lane   ~~parking meter~~   pavement   pedestrian crossing   traffic sign   traffic warden

1 *parking meter*

2 ....

3 ....

4 ....

5 ....

6 ....

7 ....

5 Grammar

Look at the picture in Activity 4 and complete the sentences. Use *must* or *mustn't*.

1 The car *must* stop if people are crossing the road.
2 The van .... drive in the cycle lane. Only bicycles .... use the cycle lane.
3 The motorbike .... turn left. It .... keep straight on.
4 The moped .... drive on the pavement.
5 The man on the motorbike .... wear a crash helmet.

6 Vocabulary and reading

Find the route from 'you' to the school. Number the directions in the correct order.

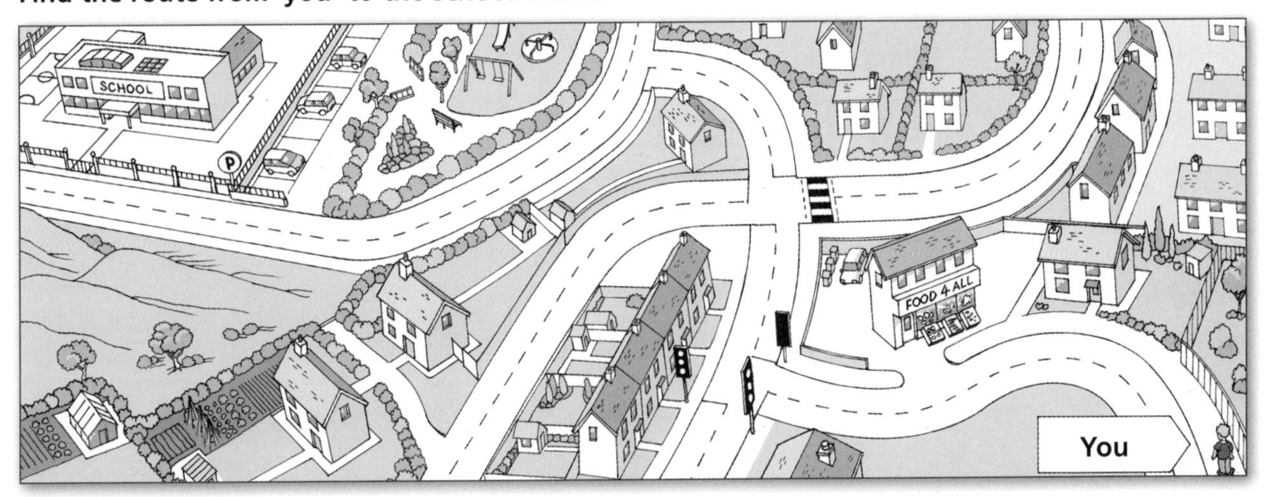

a Turn left in front of the park. ☐
b Keep straight on until you get to the crossroads. ☐
c The school is on the right next to the car park. ☐
d Walk along this road past the shop. *1*
e Cross the road at the pedestrian crossing and then keep straight on. ☐
f Turn right at the traffic lights. ☐

26 My secret identity

1 Vocabulary

Look at the pictures and complete the sentences. Use the words in the box.

artist pilot licence passport profession ~~countryside~~

2 Grammar

Write the past participles of the verbs.

1 live *lived*
2 want ....
3 be ....
4 have ....
5 study ....
6 know ....
7 like ....
8 do ....
9 fall ....
10 go ....

3 Grammar

Use the words to write questions.

a How long / you / be / a pilot
How long have you been a pilot?

b How long / Leila / study / English
?

c How long / they / know / each other
?

d How long / you / have / a passport
?

e How long / Ollie / have / that skateboard
?

f How long / your friends / be / online
?

4 Grammar

a) **Choose the correct words.**

1 She's studied it **since**/**for** 2003. [b]
2 He's had it **since/for** two weeks. [ ]
3 I've had it **since/for** three years. [ ]
4 They've known each other **since/for** they were five. [ ]
5 I've been a pilot **since/for** ten years. [ ]
6 They've been online **since/for** 3 o'clock. [ ]

b) **Match the sentences in Part a with the questions in Activity 3.**

5 Grammar

Look at the table and complete the sentences. Use the present perfect and *for* or *since*.

have a pet	3 years
play guitar	2007
study English	2005
want to be a pilot	8 years
know Rory	primary school

1 Connor *has had* a pet *for* three years.
2 He .... the guitar .... 2007.
3 He .... English .... 2005.
4 He .... to be a pilot .... eight years.
5 Connor and Rory .... each other .... primary school.

6 Writing

Write true answers to the questions using both *for* and *since*.

1 How long have you had your favourite thing?
I've had my favourite thing
for *two years*.
since *my twelfth birthday*.

2 How long have you liked your favourite band?
....
for ....
since ....

3 How long have you lived in your home?
....
for ....
since ....

4 How long have you known your best friend?
....
for ....
since ....

27 My amazing year

1 Vocabulary

Look at the pictures. Complete the sentences.

1 2 3 4 5

1 Last month, I planted some *seeds* in the garden.
2 Now we have lots of lovely red .... We eat them in salads every day!
3 My trousers are falling down! I need to wear a ....
4 I love Malaysian food, especially .... with chicken and peanuts.
5 There are lots of plants in my bedroom. I put them in colourful ....

2 Grammar

Read the sentences. Write past simple (PS) or present perfect (PP).

1 I started acting lessons last month. *PS*
2 I've learnt to play a song on the piano. ....
3 I went to Greece last year. ....
4 My uncle sailed round the world once. ....
5 We've lived in this house for ten years. ....
6 Have you ever climbed a mountain? ....

3 Grammar

Complete the conversations. Use the verbs in brackets in the present perfect or the past participle.

A: How long [1] *have* you *been* (be) a teacher?
B: I [2] .... (be) a teacher for five years. My first job [3] .... (be) at this school!
A: [4] .... you .... (live) in this town for a long time?
B: Yes, for twenty years. My parents [5] .... (come) here when they got married. Before that, they [6] .... (live) in a small village.

A: [7] .... you .... (join) the drama club yet?
B: Yes, I have. I [8] .... (have) my first class last week. We [9] .... (do) a sketch.

4 Grammar

Use the words to complete the conversation. Use the past simple or the present perfect.

1 **Emma:** I've got a new hobby. (I / start / horse-riding lessons)
I've started horse-riding lessons
2 **Ollie:** Oh, that sounds fun! (When / you / have / your first lesson)
....
3 **Emma:** (I / have / my first lesson / last week)
....
4 **Ollie:** (What / you / learn)
....
5 **Emma:** (They / teach / me / to sit on the horse
....
Ollie: Is that all?
6 **Emma:** Yes. (but I / fall off)
....
7 **Ollie:** Oh dear. (What / happen / then)
....
8 **Emma:** (I / go / home) ....
(I / not have / another lesson / since then)
....
....

5 Grammar and reading

Read Jake's diary and complete the sentences. Use *going to*.

Monday – buy a new tennis racket
Tuesday – learn a new song on the guitar
Wednesday – practise karate
Thursday – go shopping with Mum in the car
Friday – visit Lilia, play tennis with her

1. On Monday, he *'s going to buy* a new tennis racket.
2. On Tuesday, he .... a new song on the guitar.
3. On Wednesday, he .... karate.
4. On Thursday, he .... shopping with his Mum. They .... in the car.
5. On Friday, he .... Lilia. They .... tennis.

6 Reading and writing

Look at Emma's and Ollie's notes. Complete the sentences. Use the past simple, the present perfect or *going to*.

1. This year, Emma *has started horse-riding lessons*.
   She *went with her friend, Liz*.
2. She ....
   She ....
3. She ....
   She ....
4. This year, Ollie ....
   He ....
5. He ....
   He ....
6. He ....
   He ....
7. Next year, Emma*'s going to paint her room*.
8. Ollie ....
9. They .... together.

28 Amazing places

1 Reading

a) Read about these unusual holidays. Match the postcards with the photos.

1 c

Dear Marie,

We've been on holiday in Sweden for a week. We're staying at the most amazing hotel. The Jumbo Hotel was once an aeroplane! They've taken the 450 seats out, and they've changed them into 25 bedrooms and 9 bathrooms. It was my dad's idea to stay here. He's always wanted to be a pilot!

Felix

2 ☐

Hi Isamu, I'm writing to you from my hotel room – inside a sandcastle! There are separate rooms and even beds, but everything is made of sand! It was built by a sand sculptor called Mark Anderson. It's fantastic! I'm going to bring my parents here the next time we visit England.

Yoko

3 ☐

Dear Hannah,

We've been here at the Igloo Village in Finland for two days. In the hotel there are 20 snow igloos and 5 igloos made of glass. When we first arrived, it was very cold outside (-30C!), but we've been warm and comfortable since then. In the bar, I had a drink in a glass made of ice! Tomorrow we're going to ride on a sled.

Callum

c
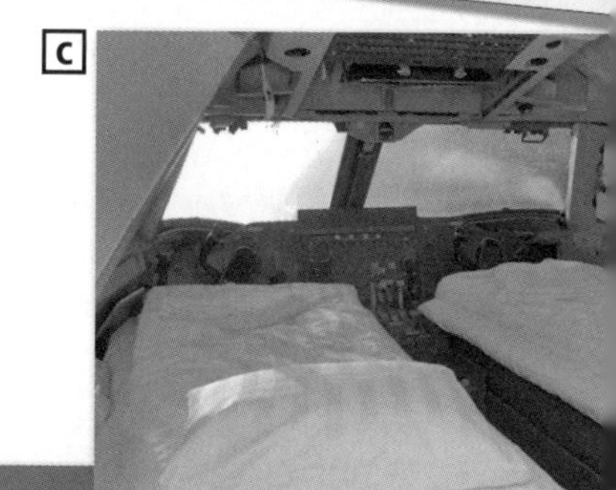

a

b

b) Read again. Answer the questions.

1 Who is going out in the snow tomorrow? Callum

2 Who has always wanted to be a pilot? ....

3 Who has built a very big sandcastle? ....

4 Who is going to go back to the same place again on ....

5 Who is staying somewhere snowy? ....

6 Who wrote the postcard in their room? ....

2 Writing

Write about an amazing place you've been to. Use the postcards in Activity 1 as models and the words in the box to help you.

been	visited	stayed	seen	amazing	big	fantastic	beautiful	exciting

....

....

....

....

....

Module 7 Learning diary

Name .... Date ....

Study tip
Vocabulary

Write new verbs in your notebook. Write the nouns each verb is used with, too.

ride a motorbike
wear a crash helmet
walk on the pavement

Write the verbs used with these nouns.

cross at a pedestrian crossing
.... at a red traffic light
.... your car on the road

Check you can do these things:

1 I know words about road features. ☐

Complete the words.

1 p*ar*king m*eter*
2 c ... ... s r ... ...
3 t ... f ... ... l ... ... t s
4 m ... t ... b ... ...
5 p ... ... m ... t

2 I can talk about time. ☐

Complete the sentences for you.

1 I've lived in my home since *2000*.
2 I've had my mobile phone for ....
3 I came to this school in ....
4 I've had this English teacher since ....

3 I can give directions. ☐

Match the directions with the pictures.

1 Turn right. — b
2 Cross at the pedestrian crossing.
3 Keep straight on.
4 It's on the right.
5 Turn left.

a b c d e

4 I can talk about experiences. ☐

Use the words to write sentences in the present perfect.

1 I / learn / to ski *I've learnt to ski*.
2 You / pass / your exams
....
3 We / visit / the museum
....
4 My brother / buy / a moped
....

5 I can talk about plans for the future. ☐

Use the words to write sentences with *going to*.

1 I / join / a karate club
I'm going to join a karate club.
2 My friend / have / a party
....
3 My brother / learn / to dance
....

Module 1 Fast finishers

1 Vocabulary and reading

Read the letter. Find the five spelling mistakes. Then write the words correctly.

Hi Stephanie,

How are you? I'm having a really good time here in Canada. It's so beautiful! I'm staying with my aunt. Her (neybours) are really friendly. There is a creak behind their house and I swim in it every day! Sometimes I worry about beirs. My aunt told me to clapp my hands if I see one. I'm coming back next winter when the bears are hibirnating!

See you soon!

Billy

1 *neighbours* .... 3 .... 5 ....
2 .... 4 ....

2 Grammar

Write sentences about the children's plans for the weekend. Use the present continuous.

1 Rory /

Rory is playing football.

2 Connor /

....

3 Delia /

....

4 Cassie and her friend /

....

3 Grammar

Rewrite the underlined words. Use possessive pronouns.

A: Oh, who is that present for? Is it for me [1] *mine* ....?

B: No, it's not for you [2] ....! It's Lara's birthday today. The present is for her [3] ....

A: There's a new car outside our house. Is it for us [4] ....?

B: No. It belongs to our neighbours.

A: Oh, the Browns – is it for them [5] ....?

B: Yes, it is.

A: Can you give this letter to Jim? It's for him [6] ....

B: No, it isn't. It's got my name on it. It's for me [7] ....!

4 Grammar

Rewrite the sentences and questions. Use the words in brackets.

1 This jacket is more expensive than that jacket. (cheap)
This jacket is cheaper than that jacket.

2 Your room is messier than mine! (tidy)
....

3 History is more boring than Maths. (interestin
....

4 Is your mother younger than your father? (old
....

5 Are you better at sports than music? (worse)
....

Module 1 Extra practice

1 Vocabulary

Write the verbs next to the correct nouns.

visit see practise play ~~go~~

1 *go* .... to a party
2 .... the dentist
3 .... a sketch
4 .... your grandparents
5 .... netball

2 Grammar and reading

Look at Cassie's diary. Complete the sentences.

Monday - see the dentist
Tuesday - visit my grandparents
Wednesday - go to a party
Thursday - play netball with Delia and Jess
Friday - practise the sketch with Rory

1 On Monday, she*'s seeing* .... the dentist.
2 On Tuesday, she .... her grandparents.
3 On Wednesday, she .... to a party.
4 On Thursday, the girls .... netball.
5 On Friday, Cassie and Rory .... their sketch.

3 Vocabulary

Match the phrases with the pictures.

1 clap hands [*a*]
2 travel by horse-drawn buggy [ ]
3 go away [ ]
4 go to the cinema [ ]

a b

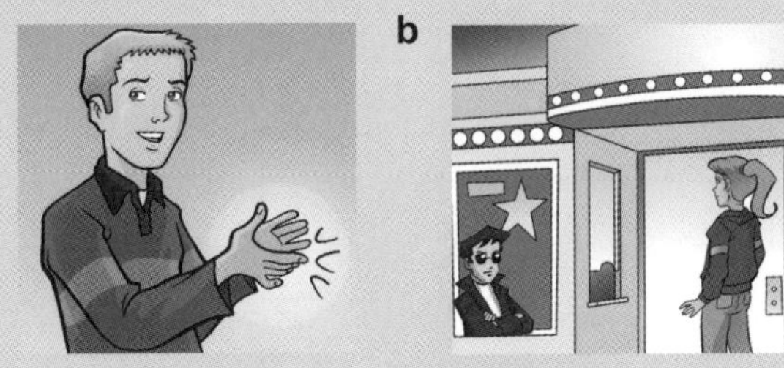

c d

4 Grammar

Use the words in the box to complete the sentences.

hers theirs yours ours ~~his~~ mine

1 It's my brother's bike. It's *his* ....
2 That's my sister's room. It's ....
3 Is this your pen? No, it isn't ....
4 This is my book and this one is .... , Claudia.
5 'Are these books .... ?' the children asked the teacher.
6 'No, they belong to Class 7. They are .... ,' she said.

5 Grammar

Choose the correct words.

I think [1] **better/the best** (circled: the best) time of year is summer. The weather is [2] **warmer/the warmest** than the rest of the year. We always go swimming in the creek then. It's [3] **colder/the coldest** than the swimming pool, but it's [4] **nicer/the nicest** place to swim and it's [5] **cheaper/the cheapest** than going to the sports centre! You don't need a ticket for the creek! It's [6] **more beautiful/the most beautiful** place in our town and it's [7] **quieter/the quietest** place, too. But not when we are there – then it's [8] **noisier/the noisiest** place!

Module 2 Fast finishers

1 Vocabulary

Look at the clues. Complete the crossword.

Down

1 To cut the lawn.
2 You hang your clothes on it to dry.
3 
4 This makes a noise when there is a fire.
5 

Across

6 A referee blows this in a football match.
7 You can lie in it.
8 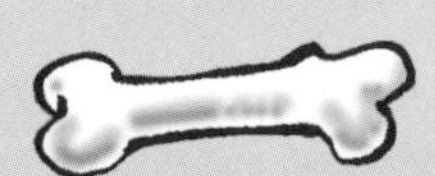

2 Grammar

Use the words to write questions and short answers.

1 Rebecca Adlington / run / in a race ✗
Did Rebecca Adlington run in a race ?
No, she didn't .

2 she / break / a world record ✓
....?
....

3 her parents / fly to Beijing ✓
....?
....

4 Chris Hoy / win / three gold medals ✓
....?
....

5 he / start cycling / at the age of ten ✗
....?
....

3 Grammar and reading

Complete the email. Use the correct form o[f] the verbs in brackets.

To: Rob
From: Jack
Subject: Yesterday

Hi Rob,

I want to tell you what [1] *happened* (happen) to me yesterday! I [2] *was walking* (walk) to school when my phone [3] .... (ring). I [4] .... (look) for my phone when I [5] .... (fall) over and [6] .... (break) my toe! I was lucky – a man [7] .... (drive) past when I fell an[d] he [8] .... (phone) the ambulance. S[o] [9] .... (not go) to school at all – I [10] .... (go) to hospital!

Jack

Module 2 Extra practice

1 Vocabulary and reading

Read about Sports day. Then, number the pictures in the correct order.

Yesterday, Kim went to Sports day. It started at 9.00 am. At 9.15, she ran in a 100-metre race. At 10.00, she swam in a swimming race. At 11.30, she threw the javelin. After lunch, she did the long jump. The last event was the obstacle course at 4.00.

2 Grammar

a) Put the words in the correct order to make questions.

1 Tom / buy / a CD / did / yesterday
Did Tom buy a CD yesterday ?

2 Christina / go to / a museum / did
.... ?

3 your parents / did / TV / watch
.... ?

4 do / you / did / your homework
.... ?

5 Frank / did / the lawn / mow
.... ?

6 win / they / did / the football match
.... ?

b) Answer the questions in part a.

1 Yes, *he did* .
2 No, ...
3 Yes, ...
4 No, ...
5 No, ...
6 Yes, ...

3 Vocabulary

Label the picture. Use the words in the box.

bone clothes line fire hammock flowerpot saucepan ~~whistle~~

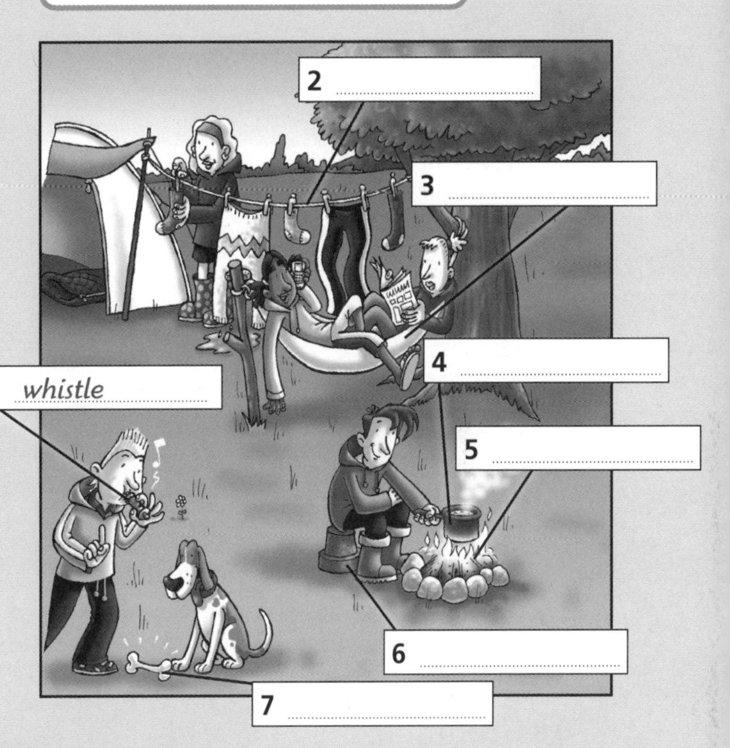

4 Grammar

Look at Activity 3. Use the words to write sentences.

1 Connor / play with / the dog
Connor was playing with the dog .

2 He / blow / the whistle
....

3 The dog / look at / the bone
....

4 Delia and Jess / sit in / the hammock
....

5 Delia / talk on / the phone
....

6 Jess / read
....

7 Cassie / hang up / the washing
....

8 Rory / cook
....

Module 3 Fast finishers

1 Vocabulary

Read the questions. Circle two correct answers.

1 What can you climb?
a mountain/a tree/hip hop
2 What can you listen to?
rock/zoo/pop
3 What can be green?
an igloo/spinach/an aeroplane
4 What can you live in?
a castle/a zoo/an igloo
5 What can you play?
basketball/a queen/a game

2 Vocabulary

Write words from Activity 1 next to the definitions.

1 where you can see lots of animals *zoo*
2 where a king and queen live ....
3 a vegetable ....
4 a house made of snow ....

3 Grammar

Look at the table. Write sentences in the present perfect.

Connor	tidy his room ✔
Jess	eat smelly cheese ✘ invite friends to a sleepover ✘
Cassie	change her hairstyle ✔ invite friends to a sleepover ✘
Rory	break his leg ✘
Rory's parents	have lunch ✔

1 Connor *has tidied* his room.
2 Jess .... smelly cheese.
3 Cassie .... her hairstyle.
4 Rory .... his leg.
5 Rory's parents .... lunch.
6 Jess and Cassie .... friends to a sleepover.

4 Grammar and reading

a) Choose the correct words.

Sonja Thomas is an eating champion. She [1] **broke/ has broken** many eating records. In 2005, Sonja Thomas [2] **ate/has eaten** 37 hotdogs in 12 minutes!

Sonya [3] **won/ has won** lots of other eating competitions. In 2004, she [4] **finished/ has finished** 5 kilograms of cheesecake in 10 minutes.

b) Read again. Answer the questions.

1 Has Sonja Thomas broken a record?
Yes, she has.
2 When did she eat 37 hotdogs?
....
3 Has she ever won a cheesecake eating competition?
....
4 How much cheesecake did she eat?
....

5 Writing

Write about the things you have done. Then write when and where you did them.

I've sailed to an island. I sailed to Barbados in 2008. I've met a famous pop singer!

....

Module 3 Extra practice

1 Vocabulary

Read the clues and write the words. Find the words in the word grid.

1 You can fly in it. a *eroplane*
2 You can climb it. t ....
3 A king and a queen live here. c ....
4 It's a green vegetable. s ....
5 A house made of snow. i ....
6 A popular kind of music. h ....

E	E	P	T	R	O	F	N	T
B	E	N	C	A	M	E	L	R
C	R	Y	G	A	M	E	S	E
A	E	R	O	P	L	A	N	E
S	A	O	H	I	P	H	O	P
T	S	L	G	U	I	T	A	R
L	R	A	I	G	L	O	O	J
E	S	P	I	N	A	C	H	E

2 Vocabulary

Use the words in the box to complete the sentences.

break play ride ~~sails~~ take wins

1 He *sails* a boat.
2 I .... an elephant.
3 She .... a prize.
4 They .... a game.
5 You .... a record.
6 We .... exams.

3 Grammar

Rewrite the sentences in Activity 2 in the present perfect. Use the words in the box.

broken played ridden ~~sailed~~ taken won

1 *He has sailed a boat.*
2 ....
3 ....
4 ....
5 ....
6 ....

4 Grammar

Complete the chart. Use the words in the box.

eaten saw flew ~~gone~~ seen flown
written taken ~~went~~ wrote ate took

Present simple	Past simple	Present perfect
go	*went*	have *gone*
write	....	have ....
see	....	have ....
take	....	have ....
eat	....	have ....
fly	....	have ....

5 Grammar

a) Use the words to write questions in the present perfect.

1 Tom / buy / a new camera
Has Tom bought a new camera ?
2 Sarah / watch / the DVD
.... ?
3 Mary / find / her school bag
.... ?

b) Look at the pictures. Answer the questions in part a.

1 
Yes, he has.

2 

....

3 
....

Module 4 Fast finishers

1 Vocabulary

Find five musical instruments in the picture. Write the words.

violin
....
....
....
....

2 Grammar

Complete the conversation. Use *will* or *won't* and the words in the box.

be celebrate come do happen ~~live~~ make write

Fortune teller: Let's see what your future will be like. Give me your hand.
Suzie: [1] *Will* I *live* for a long time?
Fortune teller: Yes, you [2] ....
You [3] .... your 100th birthday party in a big hotel by the sea.
Suzie: [4] .... lots of famous people .... to my party?
Fortune teller: Yes, they [5] ....
Suzie: What job [6] .... I ....?
Fortune teller: You [7] .... children's books and you [8] .... films.
Suzie: Oh, great! I can't wait! When [9] .... all these things ....?
Fortune teller: When you're 90. So you [10] .... rich until you are very old. Sorry!

3 Grammar

a) Use the words to write requests.

a It's hot. you / open the window
Could you open the window, please?

b I'm late. you / drive me to school
..................?

c It's raining. I / share your umbrella
..................?

d My amp's broken. you / fix it
..................?

e I feel ill. I / sit down for a while
..................?

b) Use the words to write offers.

1 Yes, of course. I / turn it up, too
I'll turn it up, too.

2 Yes. I / get you some medicine, too
....

3 Of course. I / hold it over both of us
....

4 Yes. I / turn off the heater, too
....

5 Yes. I / drive you home at 3pm, too
....

c) Match the requests in Part a with the offers in Part b.

Module 4 Extra practice

1 Vocabulary

Label the picture. Use the words in the box.

microphone guitar amp judge stage ~~audience~~ drums violin recorder

2 Grammar

Complete the sentences. Use *will* (✔) or *won't* (✘).

1 Tomorrow it *will* rain. ✔
2 You .... meet a pop star one day. ✔
3 We .... have a test tomorrow. ✘
4 I .... forget to do my homework. ✘
5 I .... travel to the USA one day. ✔
6 I .... be late for school tomorrow. ✘

3 Grammar

Read the problems and complete the requests. Use the words in the box.

borrow ~~fix~~ help switch on be lend

1 My calculator's broken. Can you *fix* it?
2 I'm watching TV. Could you .... quieter, please?
3 I forgot my dictionary. Could you .... me yours?
4 I can't find my gloves. Could you .... me find them?
5 It's dark here. Could you .... the light?
6 I haven't got a pen. Can I .... yours?

4 Grammar

Look at the requests in Activity 3. Use the words to write offers.

1 Yes / I / look at it for you
Yes, I'll look at it for you.
2 Of course / I / go to another room
....
3 Yes / I / get it out of my bag
....
4 Yes / I / look for them in the living room
....
5 Yes / and I / open the curtains, too
....
6 Yes / I / give you a blue one
....

Module 5 Fast finishers

1 Vocabulary

Circle the odd word out in each row.

1	(insect spray)	rain	cold
2	cough	bull	temperature
3	tent	sore throat	flu
4	stomach	head	insect
5	burn	apple	cut
6	visitor	muddy	wet

2 Grammar

a) Use the words to write questions using the first conditional.

1 What / you do / if / you / lose / your bus ticket
What will you do if you lose your bus ticket ?

2 What / happen / if / you / forget / your books
....
.... ?

3 If / you / come / home late, what / your parents / say
....
.... ?

4 What / you do / if / it / rain / tomorrow
....
.... ?

5 What / she do / if / she / get / a headache
....
.... ?

b) Complete the answers to the questions in part a. Use the words in brackets.

1 I *will buy* (buy) a new one.
2 My teacher .... (be) angry.
3 They .... (shout) at me.
4 I .... (go) to the mall.
5 She .... (take) an aspirin.

3 Grammar and vocabulary

Look at the pictures and words. Write sentences with *may*.

1 bull / get angry
The bull may get angry

2  tent / blow over
....

3 There / be insects
....

4  I / get thirsty
....

4 Grammar

Read the problems and complete the advice. Use *should* or *shouldn't*.

1 It's cold today. You *should* wear glove
2 It's very sunny. You .... lie in the sun without a hat on.
3 There may be insects. You .... take spray with you.
4 You .... open your birthday present before your birthday – it's not polite!

5 Writing

Write about your next holiday.

I'm going to ....
I'm not going to ....
It may ....
It may not ....
There may be ....

Module 5 Extra practice

1 Vocabulary

Look at the picture. Answer the questions.

1 Who's got a cough and a cold? *Jess*
2 Who's got a headache? ....
3 Who's got a sore throat? ....
4 Who's got a temperature? ....
5 Who's got a stomach ache? ....

2 Grammar

Match to make sentences.

1 You won't be late
2 If the bus doesn't arrive,
3 If it rains a lot,
4 I'll run away
5 If there are insects,

a I'll use insect spray.
b if I see a bull.
c if you get up now.
d our tent will get wet.
e I'll go by train.

3 Grammar

Choose the correct words.

1 If you want to listen to music, I **'ll/won't** turn on the radio.
2 If you're cold, I **'ll/won't** close the window.
3 If we wear warm clothes, we **'ll/won't** get ill.
4 If you've got a sore throat, I **'ll/won't** ask you to sing.
5 If I get hungry, I **'ll/won't** have some toast.

4 Grammar

Complete the sentences. Use *may* or *am/is/are going to*.

1 Read my birthday card! My parents *are going to* take me to the theme park this Sunday!
2 I don't know what Sarah is doing after school. She .... play football with us.
3 My teacher is always very strict. She .... be angry when I tell her I haven't done my homework.
4 I'm feeling very ill. I .... lie down immediately.
5 My parents are deciding where to go on holiday. We .... go to Australia, but it's very expensive.

5 Grammar

Match the problems with the advice.

1 I forget all my new vocabulary! *d*
2 I get headaches when I watch TV. ☐
3 My hairstyle is boring. ☐
4 I've got a stomach ache. ☐
5 I'm very tired. ☐

a You shouldn't go to bed so late.
b You should change it.
c You shouldn't eat so much.
d You should write down your new words.
e You should wear glasses.

6 Writing

Complete the advice for a tourist visiting your country. Use the questions to help you.

What places should/shouldn't they go to?
What food should they eat?
What should they do on rainy days?

You should go to .... You'll love it.
You shouldn't go to .... It's terrible.
You should eat .... It's delicious!
On rainy days, you should visit/go to/play/watch ....

Module 6 Fast finishers

1 Vocabulary

Read the clues and write the words.

1 You use it to put a nail in the wall or on wood. *h a m m e r*

2 You use it to make a hole in the wall or in wood. ....

3 You stick it on the wall with glue.

....

4 You put it on the wall or on wood to change the colour. ....

5 You climb it to reach high places.

....

6 You keep your tools in it. ....

2 Vocabulary

Choose two correct words for each sentence.

1 You can spill **a drink/water/bread**.
2 You can drop **traffic/a ball/a pencil**.
3 You can break **a glass/furniture/a cottage**.
4 You can fall off **a door/a table/a wall**.
5 You can trip over **a drill/a car/a toolbox**.

3 Grammar

Use the words to complete the sentences.

At 12 o'clock today …

1 the bell / ring *the bell is going to ring*.

2 the teacher / give us homework

....

3 we / pack our books away

....

4 Grammar

Read the questions and complete the answers. Use *enough, too much* or *too many*.

1 Would you like any more sweets?

No, thanks. I've had *too many* sweets!

2 Shall we play outside?

No, it isn't warm .... outside today.

3 Does that T-shirt fit you?

No. This one isn't big ....

4 Are you going to buy that game?

No, I'm not. It costs ....

5 Grammar

Use the words to write sentences.

1 Gold / find / in South Africa
Gold is found in South Africa.

2 Cars / produce / in Europe

....

3 The museum / visit / by lots of tourists

....

4 The children / teach / at home

....

Module 6 Extra practice

1 Vocabulary

Look at the pictures. Find the words in the word grid.

D	O	F	S	E	H	A	J	D
W	A	L	L	P	A	P	E	R
I	A	B	L	E	M	E	B	I
N	O	P	A	R	M	A	S	L
D	(L	A	D	D	E	R)	T	L
O	Y	I	L	E	R	S	A	D
W	O	N	R	A	N	C	I	A
P	U	T	S	A	N	E	R	Z

2 Vocabulary

Read the definitions. Tick (✓) the correct words.

1 a small house in the countryside
☐ a ranch ☑ b cottage

2 a house with wheels
☐ a caravan ☐ b lighthouse

3 a tall building with a light next to the sea
☐ a lighthouse ☐ b ranch

4 a lot of cars in one place
☐ a laundry ☐ b traffic

3 Grammar and vocabulary

Look at the picture and complete the sentences. Use *going to* and the verbs in brackets.

1 He *'s going to trip over* (trip over) the stone.

2 He .... (fall off) the wall.

3 He .... (spill) his lemonade.

4 The cat .... (jump off) the wall.

4 Grammar

Choose the correct words.

1 I don't like this ice cream – it **is too much sweet/(isn't sweet enough)**.
2 Do we have to do all these sums? There are too **much/many**!
3 Do you want some of my crisps? I've had too **much/many**.
4 There **isn't/aren't** enough chairs for all these people.
5 We're going to be late. We haven't got **enough/too much** time to go shopping.
6 Jim can't go to school today – he's not **ill/well** enough.

5 Grammar

a) **Find the past participles of the verbs in the word snake.**

make print read sell send take ~~write~~

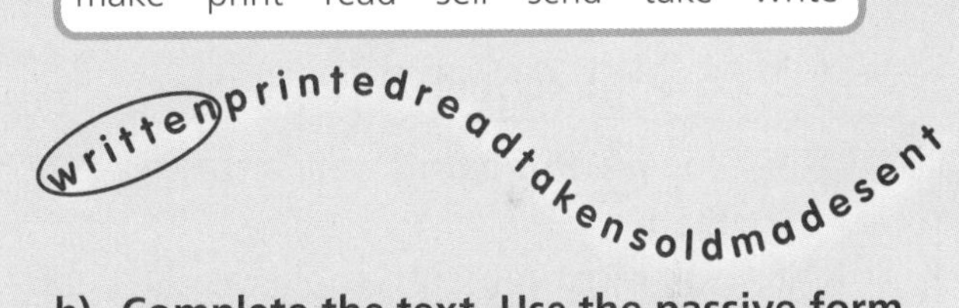

b) **Complete the text. Use the passive form of the verbs in brackets.**

Every day, millions of newspapers [1] *are read* (read) around the world. But do you know how newspapers [2] .... (make)? First, reporters [3] .... (send) to collect information about events. Then the articles and stories [4] .... (write). Photos [5] .... (take), too. The newspapers [6] .... (print) and they [7] .... (sell) around the world.

Module 7 Fast finishers

1 Vocabulary

Match the words with the definitions.

1 crash helmet [d]
2 crossroads [ ]
3 cycle lane [ ]
4 parking meter [ ]
5 pavement [ ]
6 pedestrian crossing [ ]
7 road [ ]
8 traffic light [ ]

a You put money in it when you park your car.
b a road for bicycles
c place next to the road where people walk
d You must wear this on a motorbike.
e You must cross the road here.
f place where cars drive
g Stop when it's red and drive when it's green.
h where two roads meet

2 Vocabulary and grammar

Choose the correct words.

1 You **must/mustn't** wear a crash helmet on a moped.
2 You **must/mustn't** stop at a green traffic light.
3 You **must/mustn't** park on a pedestrian crossing.
4 You **must/mustn't** buy a ticket to travel on a bus.

3 Grammar

Complete the questions and answers. Use *for* or *since*, and the words in brackets.

1 How long *have you been* (you / be) at this school? *Since* 2007.
I *started* (start) when I was ten.

2 .... (you / know) your best friend .... five years? Longer. We .... (be) friends .... 2002.

3 How long .... (you / do) drama? .... a year. I .... (join) last summer.

4 How long .... (you / live) in your house? .... thirteen years. I was born here!

4 Grammar

Use the words to write sentences. Use the past simple, the present perfect or *going to*

1 Delia / learn how to sail / soon
Delia is going to learn how to sail soon
2 Connor / plant a tree / last week
....
3 We / not see my aunt / since December
....

5 Vocabulary and reading

Read the directions and draw the route on the map. Where are you?

Cross the road at the pedestrian crossing. Walk along the road until you get to the park. Turn left after the park. Keep straight on this road past the supermarket. Turn right in front of the library. It's on the left opposite the offices. I'm at the ....

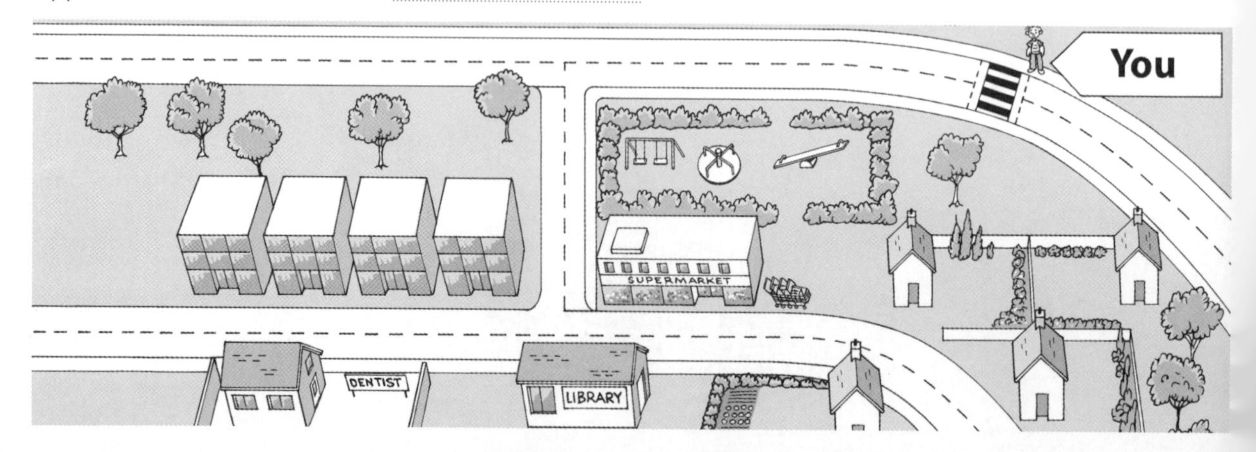

Module 7 Extra practice

1 Vocabulary

Match the words.

traffic pedestrian car crash cycle parking

helmet lane park warden meter crossing

2 Grammar

Look at the pictures. Are the sentences true (T) or false (F)?

1

2

3

4

1 You mustn't wear a crash helmet on a moped. *F*

2 You must stop at a green traffic light. ....

3 You mustn't cycle on the pavement. ....

4 You must travel on the bus with a ticket. ....

3 Grammar

Choose the correct words.

1 I've been at this school **for/since** five years.

2 I've known my best friend **for/since** 2003.

3 I've had a cold **for/since** three days.

4 She has worked here **for/since** two years.

5 I haven't seen you **for/since** last summer.

6 He's been away **for/since** three weeks.

4 Grammar

Complete the questions. Use the words in brackets in the past simple (PS) or the present perfect (PP).

1 How long *have you lived* (you / live) in this town? **PP**

2 When .... (you / move) here? **PS**

3 How long .... (you / be) at this school? **PP**

4 How long .... (you and Jenny / be) friends? **PP**

5 When .... (you / meet)? **PS**

5 Grammar

Complete the sentences. Use *going to* and the verbs in brackets.

1 Jess *is going to stay* (stay) with her friend in the USA.

2 Cassie .... (join) a gym, because she wants to get fit.

3 Connor and Rory .... (start) a band.

4 I .... (grow) flowers in my garden.

5 You .... (learn) how to play the violin.

6 Writing

Write about your plans for the holidays. Use *going to* and the words in the box.

visit stay with see go to travel by join learn how to

This summer I'm going to *visit my cousins in Spain.*

....

....

....

Searching for Speedy Smith

Module 1

Deciding who to interview

Ollie What are you doing next week, Emma?
Emma Oh, I'm very busy next week. Why?
Ollie Well, we have to write something for our class magazine, remember? What can we write about?

Emma Look. Speedy Smith is coming to the swimming competition. Let's interview him.
Ollie OK. What are you doing on Friday?
Emma Sorry. I'm doing gymnastics.
Ollie What about Saturday?
Emma We're going away for the weekend. We're coming back late on Sunday night. And the next day, I'm seeing the dentist. Then on Tuesday, I'm going shopping for some new trainers.
Ollie Do you have any free time?

Emma I'm not doing anything right now …
Ollie OK! Let's go now. Come on, the first race is starting soon.

Module 2

Where is Speedy Smith?

Ollie There are lots of people here, Emma. How are we going to find him?
Emma I think I just saw him! He was walking into the café. Let's go there.

Emma Excuse me. Did you see Speedy Smith, the famous swimmer, in here?
Waitress Yes. He was carrying a coffee to that table when his phone rang.
Ollie Where did he go?
Waitress He went to the ticket office, I think.
Ollie Let's go! Thanks!

Ollie Oh, there he is! Emma … come on! What happened to you?
Emma I was jumping over a chair in the café when I fell and hurt my toe.

Ollie Oh, no! Now where is he?
Emma There he is!
Ollie Where?
Emma He was getting into a taxi, but the taxi drove away!
Ollie He probably went to his hotel.

Module 3

An interview with India Storm

Emma Look! Let's find out when Speedy Smith will be here.
Ollie OK! Oh look! I can interview India Storm

Ollie Hi, India. I'm Ollie. Can I interview you for my class magazine?
India Of course!
Ollie What's the most exciting place you've ever been to?
India I've travelled across Thailand on an …
Ollie And have you ever ridden a camel?
India Yes, I have. I rode one in the …
Ollie Have you ever sailed on a yacht?
India Yes, I have. I just sailed from Australia to …
Ollie And …
India Wait a minute! Let me finish my answers.
Ollie Oh, sorry! I've never interviewed anyone before.

Module 4

Cheer up, Emma

Emma We missed Speedy Smith again! He was here two hours ago!
Ollie Cheer up! How about seing a band tonight?
Emma OK, maybe we'll see Speedy somewhere in town!

Ollie Who's playing at the Pizza Place tonight?
Emma A jazz band. Let's go and watch them.
Ollie Oh, no. I don't like jazz. Let's go and see the circus.
Emma I've been to the circus hundreds of times. How about going to see Romeo and Juliet at the open air theatre?
Ollie It's too cold to sit outside and watching a play is boring. I want to listen to music.
Emma Well, why don't you come to my house now? We can download some new music on the computer.
Ollie OK, let's do that.

Emma There's only one problem.
Ollie What?
Emma Speedy definitely won't be at my place!

Module 5
Going camping

Ollie What are you doing, Emma?
Emma I'm packing. We're going to the Forest Campsite to interview Speedy Smith.
Ollie Where is the Forest Campsite?
Emma It's by a lake in the mountains. We're going to sleep in tents.
Ollie What will we do if it rains?
Emma I'll put this big umbrella over the tents!

Ollie Why are you taking that insect spray?
Emma There may be insects at the lake.
Ollie Why are you taking so many sweaters?
Emma It may be cold.
Ollie Why are you taking those rubber boots?
Emma Because if it rains, my feet will get wet. And I'm taking these sunglasses and this sunhat because if it's very sunny, I'll need them.
Ollie You've got a lot of things in that backpack, Emma. How will you carry it?
Emma Oh, it isn't heavy.

Emma Mmm, I'm going to leave a few things here.

Module 6

A weekend away

Module 7

Search over!

Ollie Come on, Emma! Speedy's going to be at the new shopping centre at one o'clock. We mustn't be late.
Emma Wow! That's a cool skateboard? Whose is it?
Ollie It's my cousin Jake's. I'm going to meet him for lunch after we've found Speedy!
Emma Can I have a go?

Ollie Alright. But you must wear this crash helmet. And you must wear these on your arms and legs. You mustn't ride it on a road where there are cars. It's dangerous.
Emma OK, I'll just ride it around the park once. Then we'll go to the shopping centre. See you!

Ollie Hi Jake. This is my friend, Emma.
Jake Have you hurt yourself, Emma?
Emma Oh, it's nothing. I'm fine. Come on. We've got to find Speedy.
Jake Speedy Smith? Do you know him?
Emma No, but we want to interview him for our class magazine.
Jake Speedy's an old friend of mine from college. I've invited him to join us for lunch!
Emma & Ollie What?! Today's our lucky day!

Searching for Speedy Smith

Module 1

1 Complete Emma's diary.

Friday *doing gymnastics*
Saturday ....
Sunday ....
Monday ....
Tuesday ....

2 Write words from the story next to the definitions.

a an event where people can win prizes
competition

b to ask someone a number of questions
....

c something you wear on your feet when you are doing sports
....

d an event where the fastest person wins
....

Can you remember?

Who says these things? Write E (Emma) or O (Ollie).

a I'm very busy. *E*
b Let's interview him. ....
c Do you have any free time? ....
d I'm not doing anything right now … ....

Module 2

1 Choose the correct answers.

a **At first, Speedy Smith was**
1 walking into the café. (circled)
2 getting into a taxi.
3 having a swim.

b **What happened then?**
1 Someone called his name.
2 He ran away from the swimming pool.
3 His phone rang.

c **What happened to Emma when she was jumping over a chair?**
1 She met Speedy.
2 She fell and hurt her toe.
3 She fell into the pool.

2 Complete the sentences. Use the words in the box.

getting carrying ~~walking~~ going

a He was *walking* into the café.
b He was .... his coffee to a table.
c He was .... outside.
d He was .... into a taxi.

Can you remember?

Who says these things? Write E (Emma), O (Ollie) or W (waitress).

a Excuse me. *E*
b He went to the ticket office, I think. ....
c Let's go! ....
d The taxi drove away. ....

Module 3

1 Complete Ollie's questions for India.

a What's the most *exciting* place you've ever been to?
Thaïland

b Have you ever .... a camel?
Yes.

c Have you ever .... on a .... ?
Yes.

d Where .... you .... to?
From Australia to Japan.

e How long .... the trip take?
A few weeks.

2 Write the past participles of the verbs.

a travel *travelled*
b go ....
c interview ....
d write ....
e sail ....
f ride ....

Can you remember?

Who says these things? Write O (Ollie) or I (India).

a Can I interview you? *O*
b Wait a minute. ....
c Let me finish. ....
d I've never interviewed anyone before. ....

Module 4

1 Look at the advertisements. Tick (✔) the events that Emma and Ollie talk about.

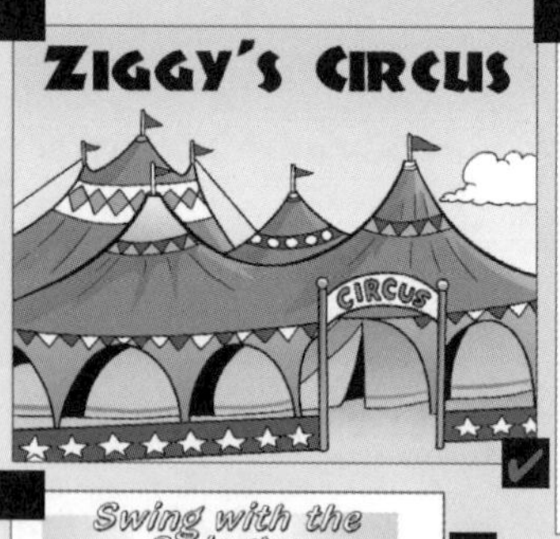

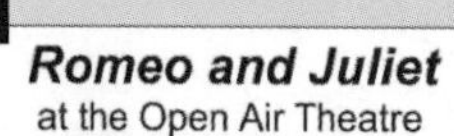

Swing with the Swingles
at the Pizza Place

STEP UP STREET DANCE

2 Match to make suggestions.

a How about — 4
b Why don't we
c Let's go
d I want

1 to go to a concert.
2 shopping.
3 watch a DVD?
4 playing computer games?

Can you remember?

Who says these things? Write E (Emma) or O (Ollie).

a I've been to the circus hundreds of times. *E*
b Watching a play is boring. ....
c I want to listen to music. ....
d Why don't you come to my house now? ....

Module 5

1 Write sentences about the things Emma is taking to the campsite. Use the words and phrases in the box.

She's taking	sunglasses sweaters an umbrella boots insect spray	because	it/there	may	rain. be insects. be sunny. be cold. be wet.

a *She's taking sunglasses because it may be sunny.*
b ....
c ....
d ....
e ....

2 Match the words with the definitions.

a tent [2]
b backpack [ ]
c beach [ ]
d lake [ ]

1 a big pool of water in the countryside
2 you sleep in it when you are camping
3 you carry things in it
4 the area of sand next to the sea

Can you remember?

Who says these things? Write E (Emma) or O (Ollie).

a What will we do if it rains? *O*
b How will you carry it? ....
c It isn't heavy. ....
d I'm going to leave a few things here. ....

Module 6

1 Are the sentences true (T) or false (F)?

a Emma won't be able to interview Speedy this weekend. *T*
b Emma's uncle and aunt live in a cottage in the mountains. ....
c Emma doesn't like quiet places. ....
d There are too many children in the village. ....
e She's going to go sailing. ....
f She wants to paint and draw there. ....

2 Match the sentences that have a similar meaning.

a There's too much wind.
b There aren't enough things to do.
c It's very cold.

1 It isn't interesting enough.
2 It isn't calm enough.
3 It isn't warm enough.

Can you remember?

What does Emma say about these things?

a shops *There aren't enough shops.*
b the water ....
c old people ....
d the village ....

Module 7

1 Answer the questions.

a Where is Speedy going to be at one o'clock?
He's going to be at the shopping centre.

b Who is Ollie going to meet for lunch?
....

c What must Emma wear on her head to ride the skateboard?
....

d Where is she going to ride it?
....

e What happened to her while she was riding?
....

f How does Jake know Speedy?
....

2 Complete the sentences. Use the words in the box.

dangerous interview invite ~~late~~ find

a You mustn't be *late* for school.
b We're going to .... someone for our magazine.
c I'd like to .... you to my party
d I've lost my book. Could you help me .... it?
e Don't ride your bike on the pavement. It's ....

Can you remember?

Who says these things? Write E (Emma), O (Ollie) or J (Jake).

a That's a cool skateboard! *E*
b We mustn't be late. ....
c I've invited him to join us for lunch. ....
d Today's our lucky day! ....

Word Lists

Accidents and illnesses

aspirin
back
break (arm)
cold
cough
drop
fall off
fall over
flu
headache
hurt
medicine
sore throat
stomach ache
spill
twist (ankle)
temperature
trip over

Adjectives

amazing
Amish
bad
beautiful
big
cheap
cold
comfortable
dirty
distant
exciting
expensive
friendly
funny
good
happy
helpful
horrible
hot
hungry
ill
interesting
large
lazy
messy
modern
muddy
new
nice
noisy
old
online
pretty
purple
quiet
rude
short
small
tall
thirsty
tidy
useful
wet
young

Adverbs

ever
never

Animals and pets

aquarium
bear
bull
cage
elephant
feed
horse
kitten
mouse
pet
sawdust
stick insect
treat
turtle

Clothing

belt
pattern
shirt
size

DIY

drill
hammer
ladder
paint
toolbox
wallpaper

Emergencies

alarm
noise
on fire
smoke

Food

cheese
spinach

Home

cooker
furniture
kitchen
radio
saucepan
sofa
stairs
window

In the garden

bone
bury
clothes line
flower
flowerbed
flowerpot
garden
hammock
hang up
hole
lawn
mow
plant
play with
pot
seed
tomato
toy
tree
washing
water

Modals

can
could
must
should

Musical instruments

accordion
amp
double bass
drums
flute
guitar
keyboards
recorder
violin

Nationalities

Chinese
Malaysian
Mexican

Nature and the outdoors

creek
desert
dark
field
fishing
forest
hibernate
insect spray
lost
moon
mountain
tent
torch
warm clothes

On the road

crash helmet
crossroads
cycle
cycle lane
drive
map
park
parking meter
pavement
pedestrian crossing
road
straight on
traffic
traffic light
traffic sign
traffic warden
turn

Other nouns

advice
birthday
calculator
diary
DVD
exam
game
hairstyle
invention
licence
mobile (phone)
MP3 player
offer
passport
prediction
present
request
sleepover
suggestion
test
uniform

Other verbs

borrow
build
buy
change
come back
eat
find
go
go away (to a place)
help
invite
listen
live
meet
shout
sleep
stare
take exam
take off
travel around
turn up (volume)
visit
walk away
worry
write

People

celebrity
grandparents
king
neighbour
queen
tourist
visitor

Performances and shows

act
audience
circus
clap (hands)
comedy
costume
dance
entertain
festival
folk music
hip hop
jazz
judge
magic trick
microphone
mime
performing arts
pop
practise
puppet
show
sing
sketch
stage
story
street dance
talent show
watch

Places

caravan
castle
cinema
cottage
countryside
eco-village
farm
hotel
igloo
lighthouse
ranch
school
village
zoo

Possessive pronouns

hers
his
mine
ours
theirs
yours

Prepositions

for
since

Professions

artist
dentist
diver
farmer
fisherman
job
pilot
profession

Quantities

billion
million
per cent
tonne

Recycling and ecology

eco-village
electricity
energy
fleece
laundry
melt
plastic
pollution
power
produce
recycle
reuse
rubbish
share
string
wind turbine

Sports and achievements

break (a record)
climb
cycling
football
goal
hero
javelin
jump
long jump
make (a film)
match
medal
netball
obstacle course
prize
race
referee
ride
run
sail
ski
swim
throw
whistle
win
world record

Transportation

aeroplane
bus
horse-drawn buggy
motorbike
snowmobile
train

Irregular verbs

Present simple	Past simple	Past Participle
be	was/were	been
become	became	become
begin	began	begun
break	broke	broken
bring	brought	brought
build	built	built
buy	bought	bought
choose	chose	chosen
do	did	done
drink	drank	drunk
drive	drove	driven
eat	ate	eaten
feed	fed	fed
find	found	found
fly	flew	flown
forget	forgot	forgotten
get	got	got
go	went	gone
hang out	hung out	hung out
have	had	had
hit	hit	hit
hurt	hurt	hurt
learn	learnt	learnt

Present simple	Past simple	Past Participle
leave	left	left
make	made	made
meet	met	met
put on	put on	put on
read	read	read
ride	rode	ridden
run	ran	run
say	said	said
see	saw	seen
send	sent	sent
shoot	shot	shot
sit	sat	sat
sleep	slept	slept
speak	spoke	spoken
spend	spent	spent
swim	swam	swum
take	took	taken
throw	threw	thrown
understand	understood	understood
wake up	woke up	woken up
wear	wore	worn
win	won	won
write	wrote	written